"Six years ago, you thought you knew me. But you didn't."

"No." Mitch's voice was cool. "I didn't, did I? But that's all in the past. I do know you now, and I know what you want."

"And what's that?" Jessica asked tersely.

"A relationship with no strings." Mitch looked down at her. "What do you think, Jess? Is it too late?"

"Too late…for what?"

"To begin an affair. A new affair…"

Grace Green was born in Scotland and is a former teacher. In 1967 she and her marine engineer husband John emigrated to Canada where they raised their four children. Empty-nesters now, they are happily settled in West Vancouver in a house overlooking the ocean. Grace enjoys walking the sea wall, gardening, getting together with other writers…and watching her characters come to life, because she knows that, once they do, they will take over and write her stories for her.

Recent titles by the same author:

SECRET COURTSHIP

TROUBLE IN PARADISE

BY
GRACE GREEN

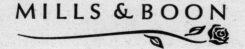

MILLS & BOON

FOR MATT HANNAY

*MILLS & BOON and the Rose Device
are trademarks of the publisher.
Harlequin Mills & Boon Limited,
Eton House, 18-24 Paradise Road, Richmond, Surrey TW9 1SR*

© Grace Green 1996

ISBN 0 263 79851 8

*Set in Times Roman 10 on 11¼ pt.
02-9612-62392 C1*

Made and printed in Great Britain

CHAPTER ONE

BLACKMAIL.

It was an ugly word...but then, Jessica reflected with a dulling of her clear blue eyes, it was no pretty thing Eric Trenton was forcing her to do.

She shuddered, despite the baking heat of the Caribbean sun; just *thinking* about her employer's vicious ultimatum was enough to make her skin clammy.

Her coal-black hair swung about her shoulders as she curled her fingers around the armrests of her lounger and levered herself up to a sitting position. Several other hotel guests were on the terrace, but they were at the far end, having drinks at the bar under the shade of a blue-and-white striped awning. She had deliberately chosen a lounger near the top of the terrace steps, because anyone using the pool had no option but to come up past her table afterward.

For the last half hour, there had been only one person in the water. A man. He had been swimming lengths, his strokes rhythmic and powerful, but now—Jessica's heart gave a panicky jolt—he had obviously decided to call it a day.

She felt her blood start to pulse more heavily through her veins as she watched him haul his dripping figure up the ladder, watched him stand on the mosaic tiles edging the pool and straighten, watched him squint against the sun and shake water from his hair the way a dog might have done.

Swallowing to relieve the tightness of her throat, she flicked a tense glance over her own slender figure, noting how startlingly her milk-white skin contrasted with the vivid scarlet of her bikini. The provocative two-piece, purchased at Harrods just a few days before, had cost her more than a week's salary, money she could ill afford—but it would be worth it. It *had* to be worth it—

He was starting toward the steps.

Jessica's fingers tightened convulsively around the armrests as her gaze spun over him. He hadn't changed in the more than four years since she'd last seen him—that, at least, was her first impression. There was no thickening at the waist, as there was so often in men his age…yet perhaps he *had* changed—Jessica's critical gaze narrowed—perhaps he did look leaner, *harder*, than she remembered…and she would never have a better chance to check on that! she decided with a bitter twist of her mouth. His swimsuit—taupe, low-slung and boxer-type—was wet from the pool, and the thin silky fabric clung to him in a way that—

Don't! Jessica warned herself almost angrily; the last thing she wanted was to allow herself to have any feelings for this man. Ever again.

She lowered her gaze abruptly to his feet—feet which were now very close to the steps and painting wet prints on the dry gray cement surface with every arrogant stride. He had scooped up a white towel from a rail, and now he slung it carelessly around his neck before starting up the flight of stairs. He was so close Jessica could see the scar from the appendix operation he'd had when he was fourteen . . .

Reaching the terrace, he lifted his head and as he did, he rubbed an end of the towel carelessly through his nut-brown hair. At any moment, Jessica realized with a fresh surge of panic, his gaze would brush her.

Now. She had to move now.

Breath caught in her throat, she bent over to pick up her beach bag. Timing her movements to the second, she paused, head lowered, hand fumbling with the handle of the canvas bag, till in the periphery of her vision, just an arm-sweep away, she saw a pair of brawny hair-roughened calves. This is it, Jess, a tremulous voice whispered in her brain; this is it.

She brought herself up gracefully, swung her legs over the edge of the chaise, and pushed herself to her feet. And acting as if she had no idea anyone was there, she stepped right in front of the approaching figure, gasping as their two bodies collided with more force than she'd anticipated, her sun-heated skin shrinking from the cool wet contact.

"Oh, I'm so sorry!" Her voice was husky with feigned surprise ... and something else, an emotion that was not feigned. His hands were on her arms, having gone out to keep her from stumbling, and she'd felt something deep inside her quiver at his automatically protective touch. Memories sprang to life, memories of other times—

Ruthlessly she deleted them. "How careless of me!" She raised her face to his as she spoke, affecting a rueful smile. "I was dreaming and I didn't notice—"

She broke off dramatically, and as she saw the flare of stark shock in his eyes, she stepped back, freeing herself from his grip. Pushing her sunglasses up with an elegant gesture, she settled them atop her head. "Mitch?" She managed a tone of utter astonishment. "*Mitch Carradine*?"

The tension emanating from him was so highly charged Jessica sensed that if she spoke again, the sound would thwack back at her like a ball from a perfectly strung tennis racket. And then, unmistakably, he took control of the situation. She saw his features relax, and had to admit to a sense of reluctant admiration; nothing, but *nothing*, ever threw this man ... at least, not for long.

He grinned down at her, his lips slanted disarmingly as he drawled, ''In the flesh, my dear Jessica, in the flesh.''

In the flesh, indeed—Jessica controlled a shudder—and what a glorious expanse of flesh it was. Tanned, muscular, adorned with just the right amount of crisp dark hair. And thank heaven that the smell of chlorine was strong, totally obliterating any male scent that might have come from him, for she had to admit, with a sense of desperation, that the effect of his closeness couldn't have been more intense if he had actually reached out and drawn his cool fingertips intimately across her naked midriff. She felt her nerve-endings tingle, felt the silk of her skin tighten. But as he slowly swept his indolent tawny gaze over her, taking in the fall of lustrous black hair, the scarlet bikini—its cups straining under the thrust of her firm breasts—and the elegant length of her shapely legs, she saw his Adam's apple jerk, and her mind snatched with desperate relief at this telltale sign of his reaction to her body.

''Well, well, well,'' he murmured, shaking his head.

''Yes.'' Jessica's lips tilted in a cool smile. ''Well, well, well indeed! Isn't it a small world? What on earth brings you to Starlight, Mitch? I shouldn't have thought this out-of-the-way island at all your kind of scene. Have you changed during the last five years...or is it six...since we broke up?'' She gave a light laugh. ''It's been a long time, anyway—''

''It's been four years, Jessica.'' Mitch grasped the ends of the towel draped around his neck and tugged the white terry fabric taut. ''Four years, four months and . . . two weeks. But—'' he shrugged ''—who's counting! And to answer your other question—have I changed? No, I haven't. But how about you, Jess? You still flitting from man to man, and taking your pleasure where it offers? Still no commitment? No . . . marriage?''

"Marriage? Good Lord, no! Why on earth would a woman want to get married, in this day and age? Women can have it all now, Mitch...or hadn't you heard? They can have it all, and they can be happy—without a man."

"But you have a man in tow, surely?"

"I'm here on my own." As Mitch raised his well-defined dark eyebrows, she went on airily, "I needed a break. Needed some time to...regroup, isn't that the expression? My travel agent suggested this little hideaway, so here I am—a long weekend in the Caribbean. But how about you? I'd have thought you'd find it rather boring here...oh—" Jessica looked up at him innocently. "But of course, *you* aren't alone! Where is she, Mitch? Your wife? You were so keen on family...I'm sure you must have married by now?"

She saw a whiteness appear around his mouth, but it was the only sign she had hit a raw nerve.

"No," he said, "no wife. The only woman I ever proposed to turned me down. Fortunately."

"Fortunately?" Jessica's flippant tone revealed nothing of the way her heart had flinched at his words.

He shrugged. "The kindest way to put it would be to say that although she was as beautiful as a doll on the outside, she was also as empty as a doll. I'm sure you've met her type," he went on mockingly as Jessica somehow managed to keep her gaze steady, "the type who leads a man on, lets him think she's something she's not, and then when she's ready to move on, drives a knife into his heart."

"A good-time girl." Jessica removed her sunglasses from their perch and twirled them in a nonchalant gesture. "But some men love that kind of a woman. No strings, no commitment...just lots of sex. Good, healthy sex."

His lips tightened momentarily, but then he smiled. "So, Jessica, *you* haven't changed, either. You're still the same Jessica I knew?"

"Just the same, Mitch, just the same." She glanced away from him, toward the pool. "If you'll excuse me, now, I want to have a swim. It's too bad you've had yours—we might have swum a few lengths together."

"Yes," he said, "a pity." His voice had an ironic edge.

"But I'll see you around," she said archly. "It's a small hotel, we'll be bumping into each other."

"Perhaps."

"As you say...perhaps." Fingers curled around the rope handle of her beach bag, Jessica left him. Running lightly down the steps, she dropped her things on a low bench and sauntered toward the diving board. She had the strongest feeling that Mitch hadn't moved, that his gaze was still on her, and she swivelled her hips deliberately, provocatively, with each step; deliberately took her time, provocatively ran a careless hand through her hair, as though she had nothing on her mind now but herself, and the sun-sequined waters of the pool ahead.

As she stood poised for her dive, from the corner of her eyes she darted a swift glance to where Mitch had been standing...and felt her heart give an odd quiver.

He was gone.

When had he moved? *Had* he stood watching her...or had he turned as soon as she'd walked away from him, determined to sever any further contact between them?

Body taut as a bowstring, Jessica executed her dive, but her timing must have been off—because of Mitch, of course—and she entered the water with a loud splash.

She was thankful, however, to be in the water. Thankful to be stroking her way steadily toward the other end of the pool. Back and forth she would go, swimming till she was exhausted. Perhaps then the nerves in her body would have stopped vibrating, vibrating with wanton desire for this man she despised.

This man who was...unknown to him...the father of her child.

Jessica's room at the Starlight Inn was decorated in a style that pleased her. The floor was of light wood and scattered with rugs in primary colors, the walls were pale, and the white cotton bedcover was patterned with a scattering of quilted flowers in lemon, emerald, orange and sapphire. A large fan whirled slowly at the ceiling, keeping the air cool...air scented with the fragrance from urns of fuchsia-blossomed flowers and carrying also a faint citrus tang from a fruit basket set on the window table.

As she slipped on the gauzy black blouse and gathered black skirt she planned to wear for dinner, Jessica frowned, recalling the phone call she'd made to Antonia when she'd come upstairs after her swim.

"Don't worry about a thing," her sister had reassured her. "Jason's just fine—you know how he loves playing with the twins, even though Dominic and Rebecca are a year older. Now tell me..." Her voice had become quieter, more serious. "How are you? Have you met him yet?"

Jessica had sunk down on the edge of the bed, tucking the phone under her ear as she rubbed her freshly shampooed hair with a fluffy pink towel. "Mmm, yes, I've met him."

"And?"

Jessica sighed. "It's not going to be easy."

"Well, you never thought it was going to be, did you? How was he? Did you talk to him?"

"Oh, yes, we talked. I...bumped into him at the pool. It was just as awkward...and awful...as I knew it would be. He's...cynical, superior, and—"

"Gone to seed?" Antonia's tone was hopeful.

"Lord, no—I'd perhaps feel more in control if he had become old and dissipated-looking! If anything, the man's even more devastating than I remembered."

"Do I detect a...wistful note? Be careful, my sweet, the last thing you want to do is fall in love with him again. Therein lies disaster!"

"Oh, I shan't fall in love with him again." Jessica gave a bitter laugh. "I'd have to respect someone to fall in love with him...and respect is something I'll never feel for Mitch Carradine."

"Then you have nothing to worry about, have you? It'll be like taking candy from a babe. He may be even more attractive than he was five years ago, but so are you! Motherhood added something very special to your looks—Mitch will be unable to resist your brand of seduction. Just bat those beautiful black eyelashes, Jessie, and all his secrets will tumble out...at least, the one *you* need to know. Now, I've got to go, this will be costing you a fortune. Phone again when everything's in the bag!"

"I will," Jess had said stoutly before saying her goodbyes and hanging up.

But now, as she brushed her long glistening hair to one side with the back of her hand, and slipped on her lapis-and-diamond earrings, she felt her confidence slipping again and she forced herself to concentrate on Antonia's bolstering comments. Yes, motherhood had added an extra dimension to her looks—a voluptuousness she hadn't had before...

She had looked quite different when she and Mitch Carradine had first met, almost six years ago. She had just graduated from university, and three years of studying and partying—of burning the candle at both ends, she admitted with a grimace—had left her with a restless energy that had kept her slim and "on" all the time.

Perhaps having a baby had done something to her metabolism. Though she still had as much energy as she'd always had, and though being a single, working mother kept her on the go seventeen hours a day for the most part, she had not lost *all* the extra weight she'd gained during her pregnancy. Five pounds...five stubborn pounds...had remained—though, thankfully, they were in all the right places. Antonia was right; she looked better than she ever had in her life.

And thank heaven for that. It might make all the difference, when it came to the seduction of Mitch.

She misted the air with Rochelle's Scandalous Nights and moved through the sultry scent, letting it drift onto her hair while protecting her necklace with her fingertips.

The necklace—a cherished graduation gift from Antonia and Fenella—was of hand-strung cultured pearls, its lapis-and-diamond front clasp nestling in the hollow of her throat and intensifying the unusual color of her irises, the deep blue with its starburst of silver. Her twin sisters had presented it to her, along with the matching earrings, in the quad after the graduation ceremony, when everyone was jammed together in a noisy crowd in the sunshine, taking photos and videos before going out for dinner. She had thought, at that moment, she'd never been happier. But just a few short months later she had met Mitch, and had then decided she had never before known what happiness was....

She picked up her black evening bag from the dressing table, and slowly, reluctantly, raised her gaze to the mirror. Taking in a deep breath, she stared, hard-eyed, at her reflection. Mitch had been right, she thought bleakly, when he'd said earlier that she was beautiful. She *was* beautiful—it was a fact of life she had accepted years ago, and she had long since stopped being guilty

of false modesty. But Mitch was wrong in thinking she
was empty as a doll. If he could see into her heart, see
into her soul, at this minute, he would be as starkly
shocked as he'd been when she'd bumped into him at
the pool. She was a seething mass of tearing emotions—
of yearnings, of regrets, of desire, of distrust, of contempt . . . but mainly of fear.

Fear that she wouldn't be up to the challenge facing
her.

She pressed her lips into a straight line and gripped
her purse tightly. While she was here, she would have
to keep a tight rein on her feelings. If Mitch got even
one hint of how fearful she was, he might move to take
advantage of that fact, and she'd have to face the con-
sequences. If she didn't come up with the information
Eric Trenton needed, her boss wouldn't hesitate to make
good his vicious threat.

Jessica shivered, as if the man's dark spirit was actually present in the brightly decorated room. And she
felt that dark spirit settle, like an ominous cloud, over
her heart as she drew her gaze from the mirror and
glanced at her watch. It was, she saw, five minutes to
seven. The dining room was open from seven to nine.
She would go down now and get settled in early, so that
when Mitch came in to eat, she would look—she hoped—
as if she were thoroughly enjoying her solitude.

"More coffee, madam?"

Jessica cleared her throat as she looked up at her
waiter. "No . . . er, no, thank you."

"Shall I charge your meal against your room
number?"

"Please." She forced a smile. "The dining room was
quiet tonight—is there another dining area in the hotel?"

"There's a small coffee shop just beyond the boutique,
but that's it."

"Oh." Jessica's breath came out in a sigh. "I see."

Her smile faded as the waiter glided away. If this was the only dining room, then where had Mitch gone for dinner? Wherever it was, it certainly hadn't been here. She had lingered over her coffee, long after the other diners had left, and now she was the only person in the dining room. She could see the waiters setting up the tables for breakfast, and even as she lifted her purse from her lap and got up, someone dimmed the lights. With frustration building inside her, she walked across to the door. She had arrived on Starlight Island late that morning, and now one whole afternoon, and most of an evening, had gone by and she had achieved very little, other than the hurdle of getting over the first meeting with Mitch. Soon it would be time to go to bed—where she would toss and turn, desperate with worry.

She walked across the foyer to the cocktail bar's open entrance, but could see at a glance, even in the subdued light, that Mitch wasn't there. Unsure what to do next, she paused by the reception desk. She didn't want to go upstairs yet, didn't want to give up yet, but—

"You look, young lady, as if you're lost!"

Jessica turned to find a man walking toward her. The stranger, dressed in a striped sports shirt and a pair of Bermuda shorts, was stoutly built, with thinning gray hair, knobby features . . . and a friendly smile.

"Lost?" Jessica answered his smile with a rueful one of her own. "Yes, I suppose I am. I just arrived today, you see, and I don't have my bearings yet."

"You've had a walk in the grounds?"

Jessica shook her head.

"Then allow me to give you a private, guided tour!"

As he saw Jessica's hesitation, the man turned toward the desk, where the receptionist was going through a pile of files. "Claire," he said, and the woman glanced up, "will you tell this young lady she'll be quite safe with me? I plan to show her around the grounds."

"Certainly, sir." Claire's eyes sparkled with amusement as she looked at Jessica. "You'll be per-fectly safe, Miss Gray. I can vouch for Mr. Wilding—I have to, actually, or he might fire me."

"Fire you?" Jessica raised her eyebrows as she glanced at the stranger again. "Are you the manager?"

"The proprietor, Miss Gray...along with my good wife, Alison. I'm Ben Wilding."

Jessica made a quick decision. Anything would be better than hanging around on her own, giving in to her dark anxieties. "I'm Jessica," she said with another smile. "And thank you—I'd love to have a walk in the grounds."

"Good. Let's go, then—we'll take a turn down to the beach first."

He cupped her elbow and led her outside, but once he'd escorted her down the flight of shallow steps, he released her, and Jessica tucked her purse under one arm and slipped her hands into her pockets. She was glad to find that the path to the beach was paved; the heels of her sandals, designed for looks rather than for practi-cality, would have been ruined had she been forced to walk on rough gravel.

The warm darkness was scattered by light—lights from the hotel, lights lining the path, lights sparkling in the boats out on the bay. It was a perfect evening...and a far cry from the January weather she'd left behind in England.

Ben Wilding, she soon discovered, was an easy com-panion, but unfortunately seemed more interested in finding out about her than in talking about himself. When he asked her where she came from, Jessica mur-mured, with a casual vagueness, "Oh, the London area."

"I was born and brought up in Kent," he said, "and my wife comes originally from Wiltshire. You must meet Alison. She always enjoys chatting with people from home." He gave a dry laugh. "We still call the U.K. home, though we've been here more than thirty years. Amazing, isn't it?"

They had just reached the top of the beach when they were interrupted by a beeping sound, and Jessica realised Ben was wearing a pager at his belt. He checked it and murmured an apology. "I'll have to go back to the desk and make a phone call. Do you want to come with me, or would you like to stay a while?"

"It's lovely here—so quiet and peaceful." Jessica smiled. "I'll stay."

After he'd gone, she noticed a bench under a palm tree, a few yards from the path, and barely visible in the dusky night. Stepping out of her sandals, she crossed the grassy area and, sinking down on the slatted seat, let her breath come out in a soft sigh. If only she were here on a real holiday, she found herself reflecting wistfully, instead of on this mission to deceive—

She stiffened as she heard voices, and seconds later she saw the dark shadows of a couple, two people walking hand-in-hand up the slope from the beach. She knew they probably couldn't see her, dressed in black as she was, and she was glad; she didn't feel like making conversation with any of the other hotel guests. But as the two came closer, she could tell they were talking intimately, and she needn't have feared they would want to include her in their conversation. They were both tall, she noticed absently, but other than that, she could see very little—

The woman's voice, soft yet distinct, came clearly to her over the gentle murmur of the waves.

"...feel so very guilty, but always—selfishly—so happy when you find time to come to Starlight. I know how busy your life is...and especially just now, with..."

Jessica didn't hear the rest of the sentence, but she did hear the man's response.

"Never too busy to spend time with you, my darling. And I've told you before, you must never feel guilty."

Jessica froze. There was no mistaking that voice, that baritone voice, whose husky timbre set her nerves quivering in immediate response as it brought memories— haunting memories—she could never erase. Mitch—and a woman. But who was she?

"You've brought so much joy into my life, Mitch. I just can't tell you—"

"We're together for keeps this time, Alison. Don't ever doubt it, or the way I feel about you—"

"I couldn't bear to lose you again, Mitch. If anything were to happen to you..." The intensity of the whispered voice sent a chill down Jessica's spine. "I truly think I would—"

"Nothing's going to happen." Mitch's tone was as intense as the woman's had been. "The past is past and is never going to be repeated. Now let's go back inside, Ben's going to be wondering where the devil you've gone..."

The footsteps moved onto the path and the couple passed just a few yards from where Jessica was sitting; the voices faded into the distance and she could no longer hear even the faintest murmur passing between the two. But her heart was still staggering from the shock of what she'd heard.

Mitch...and Ben's wife.

She sat there, for how long she didn't know, but what she did know was that—for her—all the heat had gone from the evening. Shuddering, she pushed her stiff body up from the bench. Oh, Mitch, she thought wretchedly, what kind of a man are you, that you can so easily slide in and out of women's lives, seducing, beguiling, betraying?

Back in the hotel, she went straight upstairs, and once in her room she got ready for bed, purposely blanking her mind of any thoughts. She knew that if she allowed herself to continue thinking of Mitch and his treachery, she would become sick with despair.

Yet she couldn't ignore the little voice in her head that asked, slyly, "But won't this make it easier for you to act the deceiver, knowing the man is even more despicable than you'd realized?"

And she couldn't deny herself the satisfaction of answering that voice... answering it with a resounding, "Yes!"

CHAPTER TWO

WHEN she awoke next morning, Jessica felt as weary as if she had been up all night. She had slept fitfully, drifting in and out of disturbing dreams. And featuring largely in those dreams was Mitch.

Seeing the shadowy figures on the beach, hearing the murmured words between the two, had brought back memories she had hoped were deeply buried . . . but apparently were not. And Antonia, too, had floated in and out of the dreams, because it was to Antonia she had fled four years ago when she had found out that Mitch had betrayed her.

She hadn't meant to tell anyone; the shame of it had burned too deeply, but when Antonia had heard her vomiting that first morning in the bathroom at Blue Gate—the cottage where Antonia lived with her twins, Dominic and Rebecca—her sister had guessed the truth . . . or at least part of it.

"You're pregnant, aren't you?" Antonia had been waiting outside the bathroom, her lovely oval face troubled. "Come." She took Jessica's hand and led her into the living room. "Come here and tell me what's happened."

And it had all come tumbling out, in a sobbing, half-hysterical jumble. Yes, she was pregnant, and yes, of course the baby was Mitch's, but no, she hadn't told him.

She'd been planning to tell him, she wept, wanting to tell him, but something had held her back. Though their affair was an intimate and passionate one, and had been

going on for almost a year, Mitch had not once said he
loved her. Yet, she knew she should let him know she
was going to have his child. So when he invited her to
meet his family, and added, with a lazy smile, that he
hoped to make an announcement while there, she'd felt
her heart leap with hope. He really was serious about
her, she convinced herself, and he was going to propose.
So she'd bided her time, confident at last that Mitch
loved her.

His family consisted of his brother Garth and Garth's
wife Amanda, who lived in Norfolk. Though Mitch had
never before invited her to meet them, she knew he visited
them regularly, and knew that he and Garth were very
close.

Mitch had been adopted as an infant and had no
memories of his birth mother. His adoptive mother, Meg
Carradine, had believed she was unable to have
children—yet two years after she and her husband Wills
had adopted Mitch, in the way that often seemed to
happen, Meg became pregnant, and in due course their
son Garth was born.

Meg and Wills had been wonderful parents, and
though they were no longer alive, Wills having died of
a heart attack at the age of thirty, and Meg of a lingering
illness in her late forties, Mitch felt he owed them an
immense debt of gratitude. Garth had been sickly as a
child, and even as an adult was never robust. Mitch had
always looked out for him, and before Meg's death, he
had promised her he would continue to do so, and Meg
had died peacefully, knowing she could trust Mitch to
care for her younger son.

Some of this, Antonia already knew. But what she
wanted to know now was what had happened to throw
Jessica into such a turmoil of unhappiness.

"What is it?" she'd coaxed gently. "Tell me,
Jessie, dear."

"Amanda's pregnant, too!" Face twisted with anguish, and pushing tear-damp strands of hair back from her face, Jessica looked up at her sister.

"But that's lovely." Antonia's expression was bewildered. "I don't understand—"

"Oh, how could you?" Jessica wrapped her arms around herself, her body racked with sobs. "The baby's not Garth's—not her husband's. It's...Mitch's!"

Antonia stared disbelievingly at her sister for a long, horrified moment, and then she pulled Jessica tightly into her arms and waited for Jessica's painful spasms of sobbing to diminish. When eventually they did, she brushed Jessica's hair back from her brow, and said, "I'm going to make a cup of tea. I'll be right back. And then you're to tell me *everything*."

Lying in bed now, this luxurious bed in the Starlight Inn, miles from Blue Gate and years from that miserable morning, Jessica felt tears roll down her cheeks, feeling the agony as acutely as if it had all happened yesterday. What would she have done without Antonia, she wondered, as she so often did...and without Fenella, too?

The phone on her bedside table rang, making her jump. Through blurred eyes she glanced at her watch and saw it was after nine. With one hand she threaded her hair back from her cheeks, and with the other reached for the handset. "Yes?" she said huskily.

"Jessica? Ben Wilding here." The man's tone had a rueful edge. "You sound as if I wakened you?"

"No." Jessica managed to put a smile in her voice. "I *am* still in bed...but in a sort of twilight state, half dozing, and knowing I should get up and enjoy the day."

"Good. My wife and I are planning to drive over to the other side of the island this morning, to deliver a package to an artist friend of Alison's, and Alison thought it would be a splendid idea if we were to take you along. She's eager to meet you, of course, but it would also be an ideal opportunity for you to see some of the island. We'll be back in time for lunch.''

Jessica pushed aside the bed cover, and swung her legs over the edge of the bed. This was the very last thing she'd expected, that the inn's proprietors would be so hospitable. And normally, she'd have been delighted to accept such an invitation, but two strikes were against this one: the first, she had already formed an unfavorable impression of Alison Wilding...and the second, time spent away from the inn...and Mitch...was time she could ill afford. She was here for only a couple of days, and her purpose was to twine her way into Mitch's life again, albeit only temporarily.

She was just about to decline the invitation when something occurred to her. If, at some point, Mitch were to become suspicious about her motives for being on Starlight, wouldn't it help allay those suspicions if she didn't hang around the inn on this first morning, but appeared to be keen to see as much of Starlight as possible?

''How kind of you...and your wife.'' Jessica stood up, and abstractedly coiling the phone cord around her wrist, moved to the nearby window, which looked down on the pool. Several people were in the water, several more were lounging on the terrace. There was no sign of Mitch. ''Yes,'' she murmured, ''I'd love to come. When do you plan to leave?''

''Ten-thirty? That should give you time for a leisurely breakfast. We'll pick you up out front, in the Jeep.''

Moments later, as she put down the handset, Jessica realized that her stomach muscles were clenched, gripped by tension. She took a deep breath, and, crossing to the closet, riffled about among her clothes, trying to decide what she would wear. The outing, she sensed, would be an awkward one...at least, as far as she was concerned. How she hated people who deceived, and Alison Wilding was deceiving her husband—deceiving him with a man who was, himself, the ultimate deceiver.

Jessica acknowledged that she herself was involved in a deception...but it was one that had been forced on her. And what she was doing was for Jason's sake— she'd do *anything* to protect her son from his father's immoral influence.

And perhaps, if Alison Wilding and Mitch really were involved, the woman might know what his plans were, and might just let slip some of the information Jessica needed.

The Jeep was dark burgundy, and battered-looking. As Jessica watched it approach, she felt her heartbeats quicken. This woman, Mitch's current lover—what would she be like? Would she be very beautiful? Ben Wilding couldn't by any stretch of the imagination be called handsome; but still, men like him sometimes did have gorgeous wives, and Jessica couldn't imagine Mitch being involved with anyone who *wasn't* attractive.

The sun was in Jessica's eyes as she walked toward the slowing vehicle, and extricating her sunglasses from her shoulder bag, she slipped them on. She was glad she'd decided to wear her cool white cotton shirt and pink shorts, her wide-brimmed pink sunhat and her light thongs; she could already feel perspiration beading on her skin, and—

The Jeep braked, and the driver—tawny eyes mocking, glossy nut-brown hair crackling with energy—leaned over.

"Good morning, Jessica."

"Mitch!" Stunned, Jessica stepped back. "I'm sorry...I thought...I'm waiting for—"

"You're waiting for me. Ben sends his apologies, something came up—problems with the kitchen staff—

and he asked me to deliver the package for Alison. Hop in.''

Fate was playing right into her hands . . . and who was she to fight against Fate when it offered her such a gift? Her heartbeats had gone berserk against her ribcage, but fortunately there was no way Mitch could be aware of that—though he was looking with lazy and unconcealed interest in that very direction. Her shirt was thin, and she knew that her full breasts stretched the fabric and delineated her generous curves . . . but she fought an automatic urge to fold her arms defensively, acknowledging grimly that she could use every bit of help available, in her mission to seduce.

''Thanks,'' she said lightly, and, ignoring his proffered hand, swung herself up into the passenger seat. ''Whew, it's hot.'' She stretched her long legs in front of her as far as space would admit, and ran her fingertips casually across the pale skin revealed at the low V-neck of her blouse. Watching from behind the shade of her sunglasses, she saw his gaze flick up from her ankles, to follow the movement of her fingertips as they flirted— just inside her blouse—with the upper swell of her breasts. ''I'm certainly going to change into my bikini the minute I get back, and spend the rest of the day in the pool.'' She was glad she'd taken the time to apply a coat of lipstick before coming out; now she drew her lips back in a sweet and innocent smile.

Her ploy had the desired effect—Mitch was obviously confused by the contrast between her tantalizing gesture and her artless smile. She saw his mouth tighten, his eyes narrow, and before she'd finished fastening her seat belt, he jolted the Jeep forward with a roughness that made her gasp.

''Sorry,'' he drawled, but she knew by his tone that he wasn't sorry at all. ''It's the first time I've driven this old Jeep and according to Ben she's quite temperamental, and requires careful handling.''

Jessica sank back against the worn, sun-beaten leather seat. ''I've always thought it strange,'' she said in a cool, amused tone, ''that men refer to their cars as female. Why do you think they do that?''

Mitch slowed the Jeep at the end of the drive, and, seeing the way was clear, made a left turn onto a road leading uphill around the hilly curve of this part of the island. ''I've never given the matter any thought,'' he said smoothly, ''but since you have...perhaps you've come up with your own answer?''

Jessica glanced around at him. His profile was to her, and as she looked at his strong, chiseled features, to her dismay, she felt something deep inside her melt like rich dark chocolate over a hot flame. Dear heaven, the man was attractive; how could just looking at him give her so much pleasure it almost hurt?

''You want to know why I believe men think of their cars as female?'' She made an airy gesture with one hand. ''Oh, I suspect that most men like to be in control...not only of their women but of every other aspect of their lives. And I should imagine they find it easier to dominate women than to dominate men, ergo...they think of their cars as female.''

''But *you* won't be dominated, will you, Jessica? You are your own woman.''

''Until I meet a man who respects me enough to let me *be* my own woman. Then,'' she added, lifting her shoulders in a shrug, ''I'd be happy to let him call the shots. But there's not much chance of that. So far, the only men I've met have wanted to play the game according to their own rules. Rules to which I can't...and won't...subscribe!''

Mitch jerked the wheel around sharply to avoid a stray goat that had wandered out onto the road, and as he did, Jessica lost her balance and was thrown against him briefly, before being jolted back the other way. Her bare arm had met with his for only a second, but that brushing of flesh to flesh—his hair-roughened, hers satin-smooth—was enough to send a shudder of reaction through her.

Oh, Lord, a voice protested inside her, how was she going to carry out her plan if her body was affected like this by the slightest, most impersonal contact with him? Her only defense was to keep reminding herself just how despicable he was.

She noticed he had withdrawn into silence, the thread of their conversation having been interrupted. She tried to relax, but found it impossible with him sitting so close, his brawny thighs just inches from her own slender legs. Her gaze seemed drawn like a magnet to his muscled flesh—

With an effort, she averted her head and looked down at the view below, which was becoming more and more awe-inspiring as they continued their climb.

"The water...it's really beautiful," she said. Yes, this was the right thing to do—to turn the conversation away from things personal, to things that held no danger: the weather, the scenery, the island. "I've seen pictures in magazines, but I'd always imagined they'd been touched up—that water couldn't possibly be that wonderful turquoise color."

"You've never been to the Caribbean before?" Mitch's tone was level.

"No. How about you?" She kept her tone level, too.

"I've been here...on Starlight...a few times."

"What's so special about Starlight?" She had been looking down at the ocean; now she glanced at Mitch...and saw that his features had tightened at her question. Of course. She already knew what was so special about Starlight, at least to him. One part of her wished she hadn't asked the question, but another tensed, waiting with a rather ugly sort of anticipation for his answer.

But what he did say was quite unexpected.

"Garth was the one who discovered Starlight." He tooted his horn sharply at a small dusky-skinned child wobbling precariously on an old bike just ahead of them. "Four years ago. He said I ought to try it, and I did. I liked it—and I like Ben and Alison, we've all become great friends, so this is where I come now when I need a break."

Jessica found herself cynically admiring the nonchalant tone he used when he mentioned Ben's wife. "How long do you usually stay?"

"A week at most, but I have an arrangement with...the management. My accommodation is permanently set up with all the equipment I need to keep in touch—phone, fax, et cetera."

"So, despite all your wealth and success..." Jessica kept her voice light as she grabbed this opportunity to keep the conversation focused on his work and, she hoped, on his future plans "...you can't delegate...can't get away from it all, even for a few days, without being involved in what's going on, all the wheeling and dealing and—"

"You make it sound like some sort of prison, Jess." He glanced at her, his eyes serious. "And perhaps it is, but it's one of my own making. As for the wheeling and dealing, that part of it's going to come to an end soon."

"Ah, yes—I believe I did read in one of the gossip columns that your next project is going to be your last."

The wind was stronger here, in the higher altitude, and it gusted under the brim of Jessica's sunhat, threatening to dislodge it. She took the hat off, and held it on her lap. Letting her head fall back against the seat, she pretended to revel in the sensation of the breeze streaming through her hair, while all the time her breath was caught in her throat as she waited for his response.

"The gossip columns," he murmured. "They're a bitch. But yes, the wheeling and dealing's going to come to an end soon. At least, *that's* no secret!"

Jessica let her breath ease out quietly, and willed him to go on. He did.

"My next hotel is going to be the jewel in the Carradine Golden Chain. My tenth, and, yes, my last. I'll have built my empire—not as big as some, but big enough for me."

"But surely you don't plan to retire then? After all, you're only... what? Thirty-four?"

"And will be thirty-five by the time the project is finished. No, I don't plan to retire. I intend to take a more active part in the running of my hotels, to make sure each remains what it is... the best of its kind."

"Where do you hang your hat, Mitch?" The question wasn't one Jessica had meant to ask, but it had somehow popped out. During their affair, he'd had a large flat in Belgravia, and a smaller one in Richmond, a block from his head office. "Do you still have your place in Belgravia?"

After a short pause, he said, "No, I sold it after you broke off our relationship." Nothing in his voice gave away anything of his emotions. "It held too many memories. Since Garth's death, I've been spending as much time as possible at Stokely Manor in Norfolk, with Amanda."

The pain that slashed through Jessica at the news that he and Amanda were still involved was like a knife-thrust in the heart, but it was nothing compared to the shock she felt at hearing that Garth was no longer alive. "Garth is... dead?" she stammered disbelievingly. "Oh, Mitch, I'm so sorry, I didn't know."

"No, you couldn't know, could you? He died a couple of years ago." Mitch's voice was hard. "Garth had a very rare hereditary heart condition. Apparently very few of the men in Will Carradine's family lived past their thirties, but it was only after Will died, and an autopsy was performed, that the reason—the problem—was discovered. Meg was, of course, extremely concerned about Garth. She took him to a specialist, and it was confirmed that the disease had been passed on to him."

"What a shock it must have been," Jessica murmured. "And how awful for Garth, knowing—" She broke off, swallowing the lump hurting her throat. With an effort, she went on. "And for Amanda, too. How...is she?" *And how is her baby? Your baby?* The questions burned on Jessica's lips, but she didn't utter them. Desperately, she tried to stay calm, to give away nothing of the turmoil and confusion in her heart. She had met Garth on only one occasion, that occasion when Mitch had taken her to meet his family, but she recalled thinking then that he didn't look very strong.

But now he was gone...and so there was nothing to stop Mitch and Amanda from getting married, although apparently they hadn't. Yet if he and Amanda were still involved, why was he betraying her by having an affair with Ben's wife?

Jessica drew her thoughts up short as she suddenly realized how negative and contorted they had become. What Mitch did or did not do was no longer any of her business. He could sleep with half the women in the world if he wanted to—already might have done and probably had! she mused cynically—and it wouldn't affect her. Shouldn't affect her. Then why had she felt that stab of pain just seconds ago? Was it possible that, despite her contempt for him, there was still a corner of her heart that had stubbornly and without her cooperation reserved itself for him and him alone?

He was talking to her, answering her question about Amanda. Jessica gripped the brim of her hat, her eyes fixed on her fingers—the knuckles pale as ivory—as she listened.

"Amanda had a tough time," he was saying. "She sank into a depression after Garth's death. She had so many feelings to work through, that first year." He spoke quietly, abstractedly, almost as if he'd forgotten there was anyone with him in the Jeep. "But mostly it was the guilt."

Scarcely daring to move, or even to breathe, Jessica stole a sideways glance at him from under her long lashes. His fingers were gripped around the steering wheel, his body hunched forward tensely, his eyebrows drawn down in a dark brooding frown. She saw him shake his head, and then, as if that movement had brought him back to the realization he wasn't alone, he flexed his fingers and relaxed his grip on the wheel.

"At any rate," he continued, putting his foot abruptly on the accelerator as if to put an end to the conversation, "she's happy now, happier than she's been in a while."

Conspicuous by its absence was any mention of the baby. Amanda's baby. Mitch and Amanda's baby. And of course she couldn't bring up that subject, couldn't say, casually, "And the baby?" because it was only by sheer accident—and unknown to Mitch—that she had learned Amanda was pregnant.

And it had been later that day that Mitch had taken her for a walk down by the river that meandered its silver way through Stokely Manor's small but picturesque estate, and had drawn her into his arms and asked her to marry him. She had prayed for strength...and for the ability to deceive him:...and she had been blessed with both. With her eyes guilelessly wide, she had looked up at him, her features set in an expression of astonishment, and then, shaking her head, she had run a chiding finger along his upper lip.

"Darling, I'm so sorry...I had no idea you were taking our affair seriously. Marriage is not on my agenda. Never has been, never will be. So I think I'd better not see you again, knowing how you feel..."

She had walked away, leaving him alone at the river, and he hadn't followed her. Arriving back at the house, she had sought out Garth and had asked him to drive her to the station. He had done so, without question, though he had obviously been taken aback. They had swept down the drive just as Mitch appeared from the direction of the river. Jessica had felt as if she was dying inside; felt as if she was leaving her heart behind, when she drew in this last sight of the man she had so loved. But within moments Garth turned from the drive onto the main road and Mitch, and everything he had meant to her, was left behind. He had never known...would never know...the real reason she had jilted him...and she hadn't seen him since that day, till her arrival here on Starlight Island—

"We're here," Mitch said.

His voice broke into Jessica's achingly poignant musings, and it was only with a great effort that she tore her thoughts from the past and fixed them again on the hard reality of the present...and the man beside her.

Turning the Jeep sharply off the road, Mitch trundled it along a rutted path, and seconds later, pulled up in front of a small whitewashed house in an open grassy area.

Almost before the sound of the engine faded away, a woman appeared in the open doorway. Small and wiry, her fair hair liberally sprinkled with silver, she was wearing a paint-daubed smock and narrow-legged jeans. As she came forward to greet Mitch, her cheeks dimpled in a smile.

''Mitch, you're back! It's so good to see you. And you've brought my supplies.''

Mitch grinned, and after jumping down from the Jeep, he reached into the back and hauled out a bulky package.

''Great to see you again, too, Deirdre.'' He nodded his head toward Jessica. ''This is Jessica Gray, Dee— she's staying at the inn. Jess, this is Deirdre Ash.''

''Hello, Jessica, so nice to meet you.'' Deirdre turned to Mitch, calling after him as he made for the door, ''Do you have time to stay for a cool drink?''

''Thanks, Dee, but I'm expecting an important fax from England, and I want to be there when it comes in. We'll take a rain check, OK? Now, where do you want this?''

''Could you take it through to my studio? Just put it down inside the door.''

As Mitch disappeared into the cottage, Dee turned back, and looked up at Jessica.

''You're here on holiday?'' she asked, her tone friendly.

''Yes, just for a few days. This is my first time on Starlight.''

''You're here with Mitch?'' There was a faint twinkle in Deirdre's eyes.

Jessica hastened to set her right. ''No, I came on my own—''

''Ah, so Mitch has taken it upon himself to look after you. How like him—he's such a nice man—''

''Deirdre.'' Mitch's voice preceded him from the cottage seconds before he appeared. ''Much more of that and you're going to ruin my reputation. Nice? Now there's a four-letter word destined to kill any interest Jess might have in me! Don't you know that women prefer men who are dark and dangerous?''

His grin would have melted steel; and as it flashed from Deirdre to her, Jessica's bones began to feel as if they were dissolving. No, Mitch Carradine was not nice, never could be called nice...but dark and dangerous? Oh, that was another matter. Another matter altogether—

"Don't listen to him," Deirdre warned Jessica as Mitch swung himself up into the driver's seat again. "He would like you to think he's hard as nails, but under that tough exterior beats the heart of a vanilla marshmallow!"

With a smile on her face, Deirdre stood there, shading her eyes from the sun with both hands, as they drove away.

There was silence in the Jeep for a while, and then, unable to help herself, Jessica said softly, "The heart of a marshmallow. How could she be so wrong about you, Mitch? She is wrong, isn't she?" she added in mocking challenge.

Mitch turned his head slowly and let his gaze draw in an image of her face before he turned his head toward the road again. "Yes," he said, and she detected a harshness in his low tone. "She's wrong. When you draw a knife through a marshmallow, Jess, it doesn't bleed."

What was he implying? That when she had jilted him, he had been wounded? She wanted to laugh away the idea, but somehow she found the laughter dying in her throat. He had sounded so...bitter. So very bitter.

She had set out to needle him, but somehow she found she couldn't go on. There he was, sitting beside her, so rugged, so masculine, so...tough. And yet—was she crazy?—she had the strangest feeling that he was being assaulted by emotions that he was finding hard to handle.

She drew back into herself, in the same way she sensed he had drawn right back into himself, too. As the Jeep took them back along the curving roads, neither of them spoke. He seemed lost in his thoughts, and Jessica found that her own were in total disarray.

What would Eric Trenton think if he could see her now? she wondered almost hysterically. When he had called her into his office less than one week ago, had he really believed she would so quickly manage to slip back into Mitch's life again? He had certainly made it plain what would happen if she didn't.

"I'll tell Carradine you have a child," he'd said. "*His* child."

He had ignored her choked gasp of horror, her strangled protests that he was wrong, that Jason wasn't Mitch's child, and he had gone on coldly, "If you wanted that fact kept secret, it was unfortunate you happened to apply for a job with my company, Miss Gray. When I discovered by chance that you'd once worked for the Golden Chain, though you'd made no mention of that in your résumé, I thought at first you might be an industrial spy. I was, as it turned out, mistaken . . . but in the course of my investigations, I found out you had a small child. And I did see the boy one day, when you were out walking with him, and though to a casual observer the likeness might not be too obvious, to me it was glaring. You see, I know Mitch Carradine, and know him well. You, Miss Gray, made a grave error choosing my company under the circumstances because to say there's no love lost between Mitch Carradine and me would be the understatement of the century. You would have been wiser to seek work in some other field than the hotel construction business if you hoped your path would never cross with his again."

"What do you want?" Jessica's voice came out in a thready whisper.

"I want to know where he plans to build his next— his last—hotel." Trenton's tone was harsh. "His Jewel in the Golden Chain—I believe that's what the papers are calling it. I'm sure you've read about it?"

Jessica felt as if all the blood had drained from her cheeks. "Yes, I've read about it. Rumor has it that he's got his eye on a property that he means to—"

"That he means to transform into a small but exclusive luxury hotel, one of the best of its kind in the world. He told Joel Mornay last week when he was interviewed on BBC's 'Man of the Hour' that bids on this particular property have to be in by Monday week...and the reason for all the secrecy on his part is that this property has very special meaning for him. He's had his eye on it for several years, and now that it's at last on the market, he's determined to get it, come hell or high water..."

As he paused, and Jessica saw the hard glitter in his eyes, she felt a chill rustle down her spine. "And you— you want it." Her words came out raggedly.

"I want it," he snarled, "only to prevent him having it. And you...you, my dear Miss Gray, are going to help me do that. I have it on good authority that Mr. Carradine is going to be vacationing in the Caribbean next week. I have already booked you into the same inn, I have your plane tickets here, and you will join our friend on Starlight Island, where you will use your undoubted beauty to seduce him back into your old relationship. That achieved, you will find out for me not only the location of this so-called jewel, you will also find out exactly how much Mr. Carradine is prepared to pay for that property so that I—without his knowledge—will be in a position to outbid him."

"You expect me to go to the *Caribbean*?" Jessica stared at him incredulously. "But that's...that's impossible," she stammered, dismay coursing through her. "I can't just leave everything and take off—I have Jason to think of. I—"

"Your sister Antonia will, I'm sure, be delighted to look after your son," Trenton said silkily. "After all, she has two five-year-olds of her own, so one more child isn't going to present any great problem.''

How had Eric Trenton managed to get so much information about her, and her family, without her knowing anything about it? Jessica felt numb, as if her brain had stopped functioning. Nothing made sense anymore. Eric Trenton expected her to fly to a strange island, stay in a strange hotel, find out secrets that would be impossible to find out...from a man who felt nothing for her but contempt? Oh, the whole thing was crazy. Absurd. The machinations of a twisted mind. ''How long?'' Was that really her voice asking that stupid question, as if she was actually *considering* going along with his plan?

''You'll be gone four days in all. You'll fly to Guadeloupe, Friday, and travel to Starlight by ferry, arriving on the island around midday. You'll return to Guadeloupe on the late afternoon ferry on the Sunday, stay the night there and fly home on the Monday. I'll pay for your fare and your hotel. Any other expenses will be minor, and I'm sure you can well afford...''

She didn't hear any more. Thoughts were whirling around in her head, like snowflakes in a storm, almost impossible for her to catch and melting at the touch when she did—

''A weekend, Miss Gray, a long weekend, should give you more than ample time to find out what I need to—''

''No! I can't go! I *won't* go—''

He carried on as if he hadn't heard her. ''And if, at the end of that time, you don't deliver, then I'm afraid I'll have no choice but to tell Mr. Carradine your precious secret.''

Silence strung itself out between them, the only sound Jessica could hear being the wildly staggering beat of her heart. If she didn't go along with his plan, he would tell Mitch about Jason. The words echoed over and over again in her head.

"You're talking about blackmail!" Her voice was so thin it was almost unrecognizable. "I could report you to the police!"

"But of course you won't." Eric Trenton's lips twisted in a cruel smile. "Because publicity is the last thing you want."

"What makes you think Mitch doesn't know about Jason?" Jessica asked defiantly, though she knew she was grasping at straws.

"Because if Mitch Carradine knew he had a son, that son would be living with him now." He gave a grim laugh. "Yes, I can see by the expression in your eyes that you're as well aware of that as I am." He shrugged dismissingly. "Why you've never told the man about his child, I don't know...nor do I need, or want, to know. But obviously your reasons were very strong, so I feel confident you'll go along with my little plan. And we'll both benefit. You'll have my word that I'll keep your secret and will never bother you again with this kind of an ultimatum...and you—why, a holiday in the Caribbean, at no cost? Any other woman in your position would give her eyeteeth for the chance!"

Jessica felt as if the world, her world, was falling away beneath her feet. He had her over a barrel...he knew it, and she knew it. And he had known from the beginning that she would go along with his plan. That she would fly to the Caribbean as he had arranged for her to do, stay at the Starlight Inn where he had booked her a room...and find a way to get herself back into the life of her former lover.

And so here she was now, trundling along a rutted, sun-baked road in a Jeep with the very man she had come here to deceive...

And she had only one more day after today in which to carry out her mission.

She twisted her hands tightly together in her lap as she looked around. Already, she saw, they had come to the end of their return trip and Mitch was wheeling the Jeep from the road onto the drive leading up to the inn. Over the crunch of the tires on the road, she could hear the pounding of the surf on the beach, the voices of birds singing in the bushes, the hum of a helicopter overhead.

But beyond those sounds, unheard by anyone else, was another sound . . . the inaudible sound in her head, the sound of seconds, minutes, ticking by. She had to do something, she realized with a feeling of trembling panic. She had to say something to ensure she would see Mitch again. Today. This afternoon. She couldn't afford to waste a single moment.

All at once, she realized he was speaking to her, breaking the silence that had lain between them all the way back from the cottage.

"Alison was disappointed she couldn't meet you this morning," he said. "She wants you to join us for lunch."

"Us?"

"Alison, her husband, and yours truly. They have their own private suite at the back of the inn. Go to Reception at twelve, and whoever's on duty will show you where to go. If, that is, you want to accept the invitation." His tone was careless, indicating that he was utterly indifferent as to what her decision would be.

She felt her heartbeats quicken. He might be indifferent as to what her decision would be, but he could have no idea how very welcome this particular invitation was to her. It was like a gift of manna from heaven.

But he must never guess that.

"That's very kind of Mrs. Wilding," she said coolly. "Tell her I shall look foward to meeting her."

"Right," Mitch said, and pulled the Jeep up at the foot of the front steps of the inn, leaving the engine running. "I'll see you then." He reached over and opened her door.

"You're off to work, I take it?" Jessica said over her shoulder as she jumped down from the Jeep. "Back to the world of faxes and high finance?"

He looked down at her, and for a moment he seemed to see right inside her, and Jessica had a sudden, sickening feeling he knew exactly what she was up to.

But of course that was ridiculous. He wasn't looking right inside her...she felt her cheeks turn pink as she watched his gaze skim over her, from head to toe, and she knew only too well that it was her packaging, not the contents, that interested him.

Whirling away from him, she made for the steps. A second before he revved up the Jeep again, she thought she heard him give a mocking laugh, but when she glanced around with an irritable frown, the vehicle was roaring off down the drive, and all she could see of Mitch was a pair of wide shoulders and the back of a beautifully shaped head.

Once in her room, Jessica stripped off her dusty clothes and had a shower, and then, after toweling herself dry, she put on clean undies and drew her prettiest sundress from its hanger. Icy blue, with a scattering of white stars on the bodice and around the hem, its style—spaghetti straps and square, low neckline—was perfect for the noonday heat. Her hair had been loose in the morning, but now, since the heavy black swathe was still damp from her shower, she braided it and coiled it into a topknot, which she secured with a sterling silver clasp. After slipping on her silver hoop earrings and a pair of thongs, she touched a hint of her perfume to the pulse below her ears. She wore no heavy makeup, just brushing her lips with cherry gloss, and lightly drawing silver-gray shadow over her eyelids.

Her stomach muscles, she realized as she made for the door, were, once again, tightly clenched. How she wished she had more control over her nerves! But since she didn't, she would just have to hide her fear as best she could.

This lunch, with the Wildings and Mitch, coming as it did after Mitch's own mention of expecting an important fax, would present her with an ideal opportunity to "chat" about his plans. He couldn't possibly guess why she was really on the island—why would it ever occur to him that she was here as a spy? It was the last thing he'd suspect. As far as he knew, she was totally uninterested in him, and his affairs.

Affairs. That was an unfortunate choice of word. His affairs, despite her own desperate reluctance to think about them, still managed to weasel their way into her thoughts.

Surely once this was all over, once she had given Eric Trenton the information he wanted, she could really put the past behind her, and banish Mitch's memory once and for all.

She prayed that it would be so.

CHAPTER THREE

"MITCH tells us you've met before." Ben handed Jessica a glass of white wine. "That you're old friends."

When the receptionist had escorted Jessica to the Wildings' quarters, she'd expected Mitch to have arrived before her, but when Ben had ushered her through the living area and out onto a private patio, not only was there no sign of Alison Wilding, there was no sign of Mitch, either. It had occurred to Jessica earlier that Mitch—for whatever reason—might have given the Wildings the impression he had never met her before that morning, but at Ben's words, Jessica found herself sitting back more comfortably in her yellow-cushioned wicker chair. Though of course she didn't know exactly how Mitch had described their previous relationship to the Wildings, at least they were aware there had been one, and she needn't be afraid of contradicting anything Mitch might have said in that regard.

"Yes." Jessica toyed with the stem of her glass. "Mitch and I knew each other a few years ago, but we lost touch."

Before Ben could respond, someone came through the patio doors behind them—a woman, Jessica decided as she heard the light steps on the brick.

"Darling." Ben moved forward and as Jessica turned slightly in her chair, she saw him greet the newcomer by grasping her shoulders loosely and planting a kiss on one cheek. "Everything settled with Alain?"

"As settled as it ever will be!" As Ben dropped his hands, the woman said with a chuckle, "If there's one thing more nerve-racking than dealing with a temperamental chef, I've yet to meet it! Ah, our guest is here.''

Jessica cleared her throat, and Alison Wilding—elegant and fine-boned as a thoroughbred, with her shiny brown hair cut gamine style—turned to her with a husky, "What an intriguing perfume you're wearing. What is it, dear?'' She was wearing a green Thai silk dress that skimmed her body as she moved forward, revealing a model-slim figure.

"It's Rochelle's latest, Mrs. Wilding.'' Jessica got to her feet and as Ben performed the formal introductions, she took the other woman's outstretched hands briefly. "Thank you so much for inviting me to lunch—such a kind gesture.''

Alison Wilding, Jessica decided, was at least ten years older than Mitch, yet she couldn't blame him for being drawn to the woman. There was a fragility about her, and an innate feminine grace, that would be irresistible to most men. Her skin was pale, with the texture of cream, and her bone structure was exquisite. Her eyes, unfortunately, were concealed by dark glasses, and Jessica found herself wishing she would take them off; it was difficult to form any real judgment about a person when their eyes were hidden.

"Sit down, dear.'' Alison gestured toward the yellow-cushioned seat. "And do call me Alison. Darling—'' she turned to her husband, who was standing at her side "—have you given Jessica a drink?''

"Yes, I have. And how about you?''

"Oh, a glass of Chardonnay, I think.'' Alison touched the back of a chair across the table from Jessica and sank down into it gracefully. "Mitch isn't here yet?''

"He should be here in a minute.''

Ben put his wife's wineglass on the table in front of her. He lifted her right hand to his lips, caressing it with a fleeting kiss; and as he placed her hand on the table, her fingertips just touching the base of her glass, Jessica wondered why she had found the simple gesture so moving. There had been nothing ostentatious about it . . . she knew instinctively that had Ben been alone with his wife, he would still have kissed her that way. Yet she couldn't help wondering just what Alison Wilding was thinking as her husband's touch lingered on her skin; was she perhaps remembering the last time Mitch had kissed her? Was she, even now, wishing it was Mitch who was taking a seat beside her, and not Ben? If so, she gave away nothing of it in her voice as she said, ''Tell me, Jessica, where and when did you and Mitch meet?''

''She picked me up in a bar six years ago.''

Mitch's voice came from right behind Jessica, and as she heard it, she stiffened. Turning slightly, she saw that he had changed from his dusty shirt and shorts, into a crisp, pale gray shirt and crisp white trousers, and despite her intention of steeling herself against his charm, she felt her heart give a little flutter of pure female appreciation.

''Mitch.'' Alison's voice was teasing, chastising. ''How very ungallant to give away such a secret. What will Jessica think of you?''

''She can't think any less of me than she already does, Alison!'' Though Mitch's voice was as lightly teasing as Alison's had been, when his eyes met Jessica's she detected a mocking glint, a glint that disappeared so quickly that neither of the others could have noticed it.

''What can I get you to drink, Mitch?'' Ben asked.

Mitch motioned to him not to get up. ''Nothing right now, thanks,'' he said.

''Ah, yes!'' Ben took a pretzel from a bowl on the table. ''With all these faxes flying back and forth, it wouldn't do for you to drift into an alcoholic stupor and blow your whole deal!''

"No fear of that!" Alison smiled, raising her face up to Mitch. "This one's too big to blow, isn't it, Mitch?"

"So when are we going to find out the location of the new project, Mitch?" Nonchalantly, Jessica smoothed a hand over her topknot, though she knew full well it was still safely secured. "And is anyone taking bets?"

Before Mitch could answer, Ben said, "I'm laying odds it's going to be in Spain. I've always fancied a holiday there."

"Uh-uh." Alison was obviously trying to conceal a smile. "It's going to be in North America. What do you think, Jessica?"

"I think," Jessica said, trying to inject amusement into her own tone, "that since it's going to be his last hotel, Mitch might be negotiating for a piece of property that's neither in Spain nor North America, but perhaps closer to home." With a coquettish tilt of her head, she looked up at him from beneath her lashes. "Perhaps in England?"

For a moment she thought his eyes widened, as if she had been close to the mark and had taken him by surprise, but when he responded, his voice was so cool she decided she must have been imagining things. "I'm afraid," he said, "I'm going to have to keep you all guessing, because until the deal is in the bag, mum's the word."

"Don't trust anybody, Mitch?" Jessica countered, her voice casual, but her eyes taunting.

"Can you blame me for that?"

The tension that had been stretched loosely between them ever since he came out onto the patio snapped into place abruptly—and with such intensity Jessica could almost hear it twang. She was aware of nothing but Mitch and his cold, penetrating gaze. As far as she was concerned, they might have been alone on the patio...alone in the world...

But they weren't alone, and Alison must have sensed the tensions vibrating in the air. The grating sound on the brick as she pushed back her chair splintered the trembling moment, and Jessica drew in a steadying breath.

"Let's go inside," Alison suggested smoothly, "and see if Alain has our lunch ready."

Perhaps she moved too quickly, or with an awkwardness brought on by the sparring of her two guests; at any rate, she stumbled as she got up, lost her balance, and with a little cry, toppled sideways. Had Mitch not moved swiftly, she would have fallen to the brick. But he did move, and he did catch her, holding her in his arms as easily as if she were a child.

"Are you all right?" He and Ben both spoke at once, and Jessica, who had lurched to her feet and rounded the table to stand beside them, stood frozen.

"I'm fine," Alison said, though a little shakily. "That was careless of me. Jessica—" she turned in the direction of the yellow-cushioned chair which Jessica had vacated "—do forgive me." She held out a hand—a hand that gestured eloquently toward the empty seat. "Come, let's all go through and have our lunch. I feel quite peckish."

Jessica stared, not quite understanding what she was seeing . . . but when it all became clear to her, she felt as if the world had geared down on its axis. Around her, things seemed to be happening in slow motion. She saw Ben take Alison's hand, saw him tuck it under his arm and say, "You're with me, love. Mitch will look after Jessica." She watched as Mitch, his face carved into a hard mask that chilled her to the bone, crossed to where she was standing, she didn't resist as he cupped a hand under her elbow. And in the background, from the corner of her eye, she saw Alison's wineglass, which had been knocked over when she stumbled, roll almost to the edge of the patio table, and then roll back again, the wine running in pale droplets over the edge to fall on the pink brick, staining it for a second before being dried up by the sun.

Jessica swallowed in an effort to relieve the lump in her throat, as she and Mitch followed the other two indoors.

"You didn't know?" he muttered in a low, rough voice.

"No," she managed to whisper. "How could I?"

"Alison's been blind since she was eighteen." Mitch leaned closer to talk quietly, tensely, in her ear, and she felt his lips brush her hair. "She was involved in a car accident that killed her husband. Her first husband. She married Ben a year later."

Lunch was delicious—pumpkin soup, followed by glazed poached fish with fresh oysters, finishing with a selection of cheese and crackers and hot, fragrant coffee.

Once Jessica had become used to the fact that her hostess was blind, she began to relax. Alison was perfectly able to eat lunch without any help, other than Ben's telling her, before she started, where everything was on her plate.

Conversation was general during the first part of the meal, consisting mainly of idle chatter about the island. But while they were being served coffee, Mitch sat back lazily in his chair, and said, "Jessica really did pick me up in a bar, Alison. I'm sure she'll tell you all about it...won't you, Jess? It was certainly a night to remember!"

His tone had been light, amused almost, but as he spoke, his gaze had flicked over her, his cynical expression for her alone to see. She felt her heart cringe from it, and hoped that nothing of her feelings was showing as she returned coolly, "I don't think it was all that memorable, Mitch—in fact, my own recollection is a bit hazy. Why don't *you* tell Ben and Alison about it, since it obviously made more of an impression on you?''

Ben chortled. ''Touché, Mitch.''

Mitch didn't seem at all fazed. ''As I recall,'' he began, clasping his hands behind his head, his eyes hooded as he kept his gaze fixed on Jessica, ''it was raining that night. I'd been out of the country for a week or so, and came in to Heathrow on an evening flight. I decided to call by the office before going to my flat.'' He paused.

Unable to resist the opportunity to rile him, Jessica said softly, ''A fatal mistake, as it turned out.''

If her dig upset him, he allowed no sign of it to show. ''I spent an hour in my office, and when I came out, found it had started to rain. Heavy rain, cold and miserable. The thought of going on to my flat was distinctly unappealing, and I decided to cross to the pub and have a drink before hailing a cab. You'd been working at the Golden Chain head office for a few weeks, you told me later, but we'd never happened to bump into each other. You'd been working late that night, and you came across to the pub with a couple of friends about half an hour after I did. I noticed you come in—as, I'm sure, every other man in that pub did—you were quite sensational, Jessie, with rain glistening on your black hair and running down your emerald green slicker—but I had no idea that within minutes you'd be coming over to sit on my lap.''

''It makes a great story, Mitch,'' Jessica said with a cool smile. ''But you've missed out one important detail. I had to pass your table on my way to the ladies' room. You deliberately stuck out one of your feet as I went by, and I ended up on your lap only because I lost my balance.''

"Mitch!" Alison's voice was threaded with laughter. "Such juvenile behavior for a grown man!"

"I thought so at the time," Jessica said lightly. "And if one of my friends hadn't told me earlier who he was, and that he was harmless—"

"Harmless?" Ben's bark of laughter had a delighted ring. "*Harmless?* I think you've met your match here, Mitch. So what happened next, Jessica?"

Jessica took in a deep breath and tried to keep her features schooled in a casual expression. But even as she did, she glanced at Mitch, and she knew, by the darkening of his eyes, the deepening of the grooves bracketing his mouth, that despite the apparent lightness of the conversation, he was remembering, too, the incredible sexual chemistry that had exploded between them at that first meeting. And before she could respond to Ben's question, Mitch said, "What happened next was, Jessica's friends came over to see if she was all right, and once they were satisfied of that, we all had a drink together. Right, Jess?"

Yes, he was right. And she had been astonished at how easily he had gotten along with everyone. After all, he was the boss and they were just very small cogs in one very huge wheel. His wheel. Yet by the time the evening was over, she felt as if she had known him forever.

Her friends had left around eleven, but she and Mitch had stayed. It had felt as if they were in a cocoon, with all the rest of the world shut out. When the bar closed, they went out to the street together, he had hailed a cab, and had dropped her off at her flat; she hadn't invited him in, and she was sure he hadn't expected her to. But next day, a Saturday, he phoned and invited her out for dinner that evening. And that had been the beginning...

"Yes." There was a faint huskiness in her voice. "That's right, Mitch. We all had a drink together."

"So," Ben said, "do you still work for Mitch's Golden Chain, Jessica?"

She had been prepared for this, that she might be asked about her job, but it was imperative that she keep any relevant information from Mitch. He must never find out where she worked, or lived. If, after she left Starlight, he ever found out why she'd really been there, he would hunt her down and seek vengeance...and if he found her, he would certainly discover she had a child.

"No. I moved from the area the following year." Jessica sat back in her seat as the waitress poured her coffee. "And had to find another job."

"What do you do, dear?" It was Alison who asked the question.

Jessica turned to look at her as she said, "Secretarial work." She saw Ben lean forward, knew he was about to pursue the matter, but before he could, she grimaced and went on. "But I promised myself I wouldn't talk about work, or even think about it while I'm here. That would defeat the purpose of my holiday, wouldn't it?"

Ben sat back, his cheery face creased in a grin. "A woman with her head screwed on the right way. You like to keep work and play separate—not like our friend here—" he glanced at Mitch "—who can't seem to tear himself away from his fax machine for longer than an hour at a time!"

"Wrong!" Mitch pushed back his chair and stretched. "I'm taking the next couple of days off. I've made my move, and there's nothing I can do now but...wait."

"Look at the man," Ben said admiringly. "Anybody else would be wound up to the nines, with so much at stake, but you, Mitch, look as cool as the proverbial cucumber."

"He thrives on it," Alison added. "On all the suspense. And since you're taking a break, why don't you and Jessica spend the afternoon together?"

"Alison." Jessica injected a chuckle into her voice. "You sound like a mother anxious to get a date for her gangly teenager!" Spending time with Mitch was, of course, the very thing she needed to do, but she had to make sure she left him with the opposite impression. Airily, she glanced at him and felt a twinge of surprise when she saw the expression of shock in his eyes—shock at what she'd said? But why? Surely she'd treated the matter lightly enough that Alison wouldn't be offended by her teasing comment?

"Believe me," she hastened to add, "I'm more than happy to be on my own. I'm one of those lucky people who enjoy their own company."

"No, Alison's right." Mitch had made a quick recovery; his tone was silky. "We're both on holiday, and we should take advantage of that. Why don't we have a siesta, and then we can meet afterward and have a swim together—?"

"Wonderful idea!" Ben pushed back his chair and got up, and then assisted Alison as she got to her feet, too.

Everything, Jessica reflected, was going her way—not the way she wanted it to be, but the way it had to be, if she was to find out what Eric Trenton needed to know.

She allowed Mitch to escort her from the dining room, and after she had thanked Ben and Alison for lunch, he ushered her out and along the lobby to the foyer.

"Will an hour be long enough for you?" He stood with her by the elevator.

"Mmm." The elevator arrived and she stepped in. He didn't follow. "Aren't you going up to your room?" She drew her brows together in a small frown.

"I have a chalet in the grounds," he said, and as the doors started to glide closed, he added with a lazy smile, "If you're good, I may invite you to see it sometime."

*   *   *

Once in her room, Jessica went straight to the phone by her bed and spent the next five minutes talking with Antonia and Jason.

Everything was fine, Antonia told her, and Jason's happy tone reinforced Antonia's assurances. Jessica winced as she laid down the handset after Jason's hasty, "Bye, Mummy. I've got to go. Dominic's waiting to play." The sound of his voice had made her heart ache as surely as if his small hand had been squeezing it. She would do anything—*anything*—to keep his father from finding out about him.

As she crossed to the built-in closet, she caught sight of her reflection in the mirror and was taken aback by the expression on her face. Her mouth was compressed into a tight, ugly line, an indication of the stress she was under. She'd have to loosen up before she joined Mitch later...but she was aware how very difficult that was going to be.

She knew she ought to lie down, but she also knew she was far too uptight to rest. She slid open the closet door, and riffled about among the lightweight clothes dangling from their hangers. Projecting the right image to Mitch this afternoon was of the ultimate importance.

She'd purposely worn the scarlet bikini for their first meeting, knowing he'd have no reason to think that meeting was other than pure coincidence, and because of that, he'd have no reason to suspect that she'd worn the bikini for the express purpose of exciting him sexually. If she wore it again—or anything that was just as blatantly designed to make male hormones run amok— he would surely suspect she was trying to turn him on...which, of course, she was. But what she *wanted* him to believe, initially at any rate, was that she had no interest whatsoever in him, and had no interest in dressing to attract him. Therefore...

Narrowing her eyes, she slipped her black maillot from its hanger. She knew very well that flesh hidden from the eye could be far more tantalizing to men than flesh exposed; and she knew, also, that the black maillot—which looked deceptively prim and proper on its hanger—took on a whole new life once it molded itself to her voluptuous body. Yet it was neither low-cut at the breasts not high-cut at the thighs; it was, one could argue, the epitome of modesty...

She had modeled it for Antonia the night before leaving for the island, and her sister's eyes had sparkled.

"Atta girl!" she'd said approvingly. "And I wish I could be on Starlight when you wear it. You're going to knock that treacherous so-and-so's socks off."

Jessica's lips twisted bleakly as she went into the bathroom. She might have to knock more than Mitch's socks off before she found out what she wanted to know...but if that's what it took, then that's what she would do.

She was ready far too early, and found herself pacing back and forth in the bedroom. After putting on the black maillot, she'd slipped into a gathered cotton skirt in a small black-and-white geometric pattern, and a black T-shirt, that she'd tucked in at the waist. She looked, she knew, impeccable...perhaps even stark. With her black hair scraped back into a severe ponytail, her face scrubbed clean, and no jewelry except silver stud earrings, nothing about her appearance even hinted at seduction.

Yet.

She'd heard people talk about having butterflies in their stomachs when they were nervous; that, she acknowledged, would be a totally inadequate description of how she felt. No way could butterflies survive in her stomach, tightly knotted as its muscles were. How about

a bunch of Sumo wrestlers grappling in her stomach?
Yes, that was more like it.

Restlessly she moved around the room one last time,
and then decided she could stay up there no longer. She
had to do something—perhaps go for a walk in the
grounds—anything to take her mind off Mitch, and the
problems facing her. After a last glance at her reflection
in the mirror, she dropped her sunglasses into the pocket
of her skirt, scooped up her capacious beach bag, and
made for the door.

When she came out of the elevator, to her surprise
the first person she saw in the foyer was Mitch. He was
sitting with a young couple in the area over by the
window. The three were absorbed in conversation, but
when he noticed her, his eyebrows shot up. He glanced
at his watch, and she saw him grimace, and after a few
quick words to his companions, he got up and came over
to join her.

"My apologies—just after you went upstairs, I
bumped into the Latimers. Maria worked in one of my
hotels before she met Ken...I haven't seen them since
their wedding day four years ago. We were just catching
up with each other, and—" he rubbed the heel of one
hand across his shadowed jaw "—as you can see, I'm
not ready."

"That's all right," Jessica murmured stiffly. "I'm
early."

"No problem." He caught hold of her forearm,
loosely. "Come to the chalet with me—I have to go over
for my swim trunks...and—" his tawny gaze slid
mockingly to meet her eyes "—a shave, if you think I'm
going to need it."

"You look fine to me," Jessica said, her airy tone
giving no sign that she knew only too well what he was
thinking, knew only too well what he was remembering.
Only hours after he shaved, Mitch's jaw always became

rough and abrasive as sandpaper, and during the months
of their relationship, because Jessica's skin was very sensitive—something Mitch soon discovered—he had always
made a point of shaving just before they went out on a
date. "In fact," she went on now, in the same airy tone,
"you look...rakish, with that fungal growth. Rather
fitting, actually."

He had led her to the foyer's side door, and as they
walked out into the heat of the afternoon, he laughed
dryly.

"Are you implying that my morals leave something
to be desired, Jessica, just because I have a bit of a beard?
What would you think..." still holding her forearm, he
guided her along a path edged by beds of hibiscus shrubs
with showy blossoms of orange, red, and apricot "...if
I were to imply that, just because you're here alone,
you've come to look for a wealthy husband?"

"I'd say you were putting one and one together and
coming up with five." Jessica's voice was tart. "I'm here
on holiday, period."

"A pretty *rich* holiday, isn't it, for a secretary?" He
slid his hand down her bare forearm and she thought he
was going to release her; instead, he trapped her further
by circling her delicate wrist tightly with his fingers.

Jessica shrugged. "People make choices, Mitch. I
work hard all year, and if I choose to scrimp on other
things, and blow all my savings on one good vacation,
albeit a short one, that's my decision to make." If only
he knew, she reflected tautly, that every penny of her
savings was invested with a view to paying for Jason's
future education, and that her hotel bill on Starlight was
being paid for by a man she despised.

"I find it odd," he went on thoughtfully, as if he
hadn't listened to a word she'd said, "that you did come
here alone. The Jessica I knew wasn't a loner. She'd never
have dreamed of planning something like this—"

"Something like what?" The pressure of his thumb and fingers around her wrist was disturbing...more than disturbing. The pad of his thumb was rubbing on sensitive skin at her inner wrist, resulting in shivers of sensation dancing up her arm...and making her heartbeats take off in a crazy race to nowhere.

"Like...traveling abroad, to a place she'd never been before, by herself."

"You thought you knew me, Mitch, but you didn't."

"No." His voice was cool. "I didn't, did I? But you certainly set me straight that day we spent at Stokely Manor with Garth and Amanda. At any rate, that's all in the past. I do know you now, and I do know what you want—"

"And what's that?" she asked tersely.

"A relationship with no strings." His features twisted wryly. "There's something you probably never guessed, Jess. I often thought about you after you left, and I wished you hadn't disappeared so completely off the face of the earth."

"Any why was that?"

"Because...if we'd had the chance to talk again, once I got over the shock of finding out you were—what did you call it, 'a good-time girl'?—we could have started fresh, started a new relationship on completely different terms. I'd have set you up in my place in Belgravia. You could have kept one night of the week free for me—perhaps a Friday—and for the rest..." He released her wrist but caught her hand in his before it could fall, and wove his long fingers through her slender ones. "You would have been free to live your life as you pleased. No strings—no questions asked."

While he had been talking, they had been approaching a pretty chalet, its walls almost hidden behind a tumble of bougainvillea vines with bracts of a vibrant bluish purple. The front door was pale violet, and enormous scarlet roses rambled over a weathered trellis arching above the entryway.

Mitch paused under the trellis, and looked down at her. "What do you think, Jess? Is it too late?"

"Too late... for what?" The scent of roses was rich in her nostrils, and so sweet it was like a taste of heaven.

"Too late to begin an affair." He lifted her hand to his lips and brushed a kiss across her knuckles. "A new affair. My flat's gone, but we can choose another, choose it together. What do you say, Jess? Are you for it?"

Was he serious? It was impossible to tell; his eyes were shuttered, giving absolutely nothing away. But Jessica felt a strange hysteria building up inside her. Had he, when they first met almost six years ago, offered her such a deal, she had been so utterly besotted with him she'd have had no hesitation about saying "yes." One night a week with Mitch Carradine—it would have been only a crumb, but she would have settled for it. And there would have been an honesty about it, right from the beginning. An affair, and not a serious one. No commitment, on either side.

But so much had happened following their first meeting! She had fallen hopelessly in love with him; she had become pregnant with his child; and she had discovered that all the time he had been making love to her, he had been deceiving her. The man was contemptible. Oh, certainly, as she'd listened to his offer just now, she had felt her body react to the invitation. One night a week with him, one whole night, to do nothing but make love. But it wouldn't be love... was never love on his part, could never again be love on hers.

But she couldn't let him suspect what an offensive offer she found it, nor how she wanted to throw it back in his face.

She withdrew her hand from his grasp, and leaned back against the edge of the door. "Well," she mused, her mouth curving in a slow smile as she looked up at him from beneath her thick, coal-black lashes, ''that's something to think about—isn't it?—for the cold winter nights ahead. Do I have to give you my answer now, Mitch, or may I think it over?''

A flicker of something passed across his eyes, but it was gone so quickly she had no idea what it signified. Emotion of some sort, of course, but it could have been scorn, triumph, pain. She didn't know; would never know. Didn't care to know.

''No rush, Jess. You have all the time in the world. I'd like to have you back in my life again...on any terms.''

''That's very...generous...of you...''

He unlocked the door and pushed it open. ''I'm a generous man—just how generous I can be, you'll find out if you accept my offer. Now, would you like to—?''

''Come into your parlor?'' Jessica shook her head. ''No, thanks, Mitch. This fly—I think—would be safer, for the moment, if she were to wait outside.''

He chuckled. ''In that case, this...spider will be as fast as he can. Don't go away.''

Oh, she had no intention of going away! Jessica slipped her hands into her pockets as she wandered around the chalet's garden, inhaling the exotic scents that mingled with the salty ocean air. Mitch could never know just how eager she was to see the inside of his temporary domain, could never know how she'd had to restrain herself when he'd invited her in. But she would get inside, when it suited her, and she would make it seem as though he had persuaded her against his will.

What was it Ben had said about all those faxes flying back and forth? What a wealth of information would be on those printed papers. If only she could get a glimpse—just a glimpse—so she could get an idea of what was going on. But she mustn't rush things, mustn't risk making him suspicious. She would tease and tantalize Mitch today, but she would lead him only so far. Tomorrow, she would pretend to weaken, and allow him to coax her into the chalet.

She raised her face to the sun, her eyes closed, and let the heat seep into her bones. It was sheer bliss, the warmth on her cheeks and brow, the gentle flutter of her skirt around her calves, the sound of the ocean mingling with the call of the gulls.

She wasn't sure how long she stood there, dreaming, before she heard Mitch's voice come from behind her.

"Ready?" he asked.

She turned around, forcing a smile, a smile that died slowly when she saw him.

And her blood began a slow, heavy drumbeat along her veins.

CHAPTER FOUR

MITCH had showered and shaved, and was now wearing a pair of denim cutoffs and an unbuttoned shirt with his sunglasses stuck in the breast pocket . . . and male sexuality exuded from every pore of his body with such impact Jessica felt as dazed as if she'd been struck by lightning.

He grinned at her, his golden eyes twinkling. "Don't stand there with your mouth open, Jess. You look for all the world like a fledgling waiting for a worm."

With an effort, Jessica regained control of herself, while cursing that part of her that had reacted so visibly to Mitch and his raw male magnetism. Affecting an amused smile, she said, implication obvious in her tone, "*So?*"

His laugh rolled out. "A worm, am I, Jess? Why on earth would you want to spend time with such a lowly creature?"

He had come right up to her as he spoke and was so close she could smell the lingering hint of his shaving cream. Gillette Foamy, regular. The same brand he'd used when she'd known him before. And as she inhaled the scent, a fragment of memory, as unwelcome as it was unexpected, flashed into her mind.

It was so vivid it swept her backward through time as if she were on a magic carpet: the memory of the two of them together, the morning after they'd made love for the very first time, at his flat in Belgravia.

Mitch with a towel around his waist, drawing the last scrape of his razor over his jaw as he finished shaving.

60

She standing behind him, naked, her arms clasped around him, her lips pressed against the damp skin of his shoulder.

Their eyes meeting in the patch of bathroom mirror he'd wiped clean with his towel after their shower, his tawny gaze darkening swiftly with rekindled desire...

He'd put down his razor and with a groan had turned and drawn her roughly into his arms. And when they'd kissed, his jaw had been smooth as silk, and his body scent had mingled with the scent of his shaving cream, and she—her senses adrift on a heady cloud of excitement and anticipation—had yielded breathlessly as he'd swept her up and carried her back to bed—

A stab of painful longing slashed through her now but even as she winced from it, she thrust the memories aside. Swiveling away from Mitch, she began walking along the path in the direction of the swimming pool. He would only have to look into her eyes, she knew, to see how much she wanted him. And she acknowledged to herself that she had known from that first encounter the previous day that the old chemistry still sparked dangerously between them, and he wouldn't be Mitch if he didn't react to that look in her eyes and drag her into his arms. She was well aware that if he did, she wouldn't be able to resist him...and she wasn't ready, yet, to let him come so close.

In a moment or two, she felt in control again, and as she steeled herself, she groped in her skirt pocket for her sunglasses and put them on. At least, no matter how hard he looked, he wouldn't be able to see her eyes—

"Jess, hold on—we're not going that way."

She turned. "But I thought we'd go to the pool." Her voice had a husky edge. "Or down to the water."

"I have the Jeep. The Wildings own another private beach a mile or so along the coast—it'll give us a chance to be on our own."

Oh, great! Jessica thought with a sense of bleak despair. Just what I need, to be alone, in some secluded spot with this man who can melt my bones just by conjuring himself up in my memories. She took in a deep breath, and, pasting on a bright smile, said, ''Oh, lovely. Let's go.''

Mitch didn't talk much during the short trip, and Jessica was free to look about her, free to admire the scenery.

The road was dusty and rutted, and looming from it to the left were high-peaked hills, the lower slopes richly verdant with palms and tropical vines, the upper slopes hazing into a soft lilac color as they rose to meet the azure sky. To the right was the ocean, the blue-green water shimmering in the afternoon heat, the sparkling white beaches fringed with groves of palms and mangrove thickets that rooted their way right to the water's edge.

At one point they drove past fields of sugarcane. At another, past a magnificent white stucco house set above the ocean, its beautifully manicured lawns edged by a profusion of anthuriums and hibiscus. And just two minutes later, past a tiny cottage at the roadside, with a corrugated roof and white-painted fretwork, its walls brilliant with the rosy red blooms of bougainvillea, its side yard teeming with laughing dark-skinned children and playfully barking dogs.

Jessica found herself charmed by all of it, and she was lazily watching a frigate bird gliding overhead when Mitch wheeled the Jeep suddenly to the right, his unexpected move taking her by surprise. Frowning, she glanced ahead, and blinked as she saw they were making for what seemed to be an impenetrable jungle.

Mitch must have sensed her unease, because he muttered something that sounded like ''concealed entrance.'' Jessica held her breath as he battered the Jeep through a tangle of creepers and felt no more relaxed when they came out the other side and he guided the ancient vehicle along a narrow trail under a canopy of greenery that choked out the sun.

"I hope you know where you're going," she grumbled.

"O, ye of little faith." In the shadows, Mitch's gaze met hers, and she saw a taunting glint. "I know where I'm going, Jessica. The point is..." His tone was light. "Do you?"

He moved his gaze back to the trail ahead, and had Jessica not noticed the darkening of his eyes as he asked the question, she'd have thought it a casual one. But she *had* noticed that sudden change in his expression, and she knew his nonchalance was only superficial. What on earth could he mean? she wondered. *Did she know where she was going?* She decided it would be best to take his question literally, as if she believed that was how he had meant it.

"Of course I know where I'm going. You're taking me to the beach, aren't you?"

Jessica thought his grip on the wheel tightened.

"Jess," he said quietly, "you're a puzzle to me."

"I am? In what way?"

He shook his head, and she saw his lips twitch, but it wasn't a smile, not a real smile. "In the old days, I could read you like a book—your eyes were always so clear and honest—no secrets, no devious thoughts. But now..." He glanced at her again. "I can't read you at all."

"That's all to the good, then, isn't it?" she said flippantly. "If I decide to take you up on your offer of an affair, our relationship will have so much more spice—a woman should always retain an aura of mystery if she wants to keep the man in her life interested."

"But if you take me up on my offer, I won't be the 'man in your life,' will I, Jess? I'll just be one of many—

no, don't protest.'' He held out a hand to silence her as
she opened her mouth to choke out an indignant denial.
''That's no problem. You'll not be the only woman in
my life. Our relationship therefore won't require that I
see you through a lover's rose-tinted glasses, and it won't
require that I be enthralled by your feminine mystique.
What I'll be interested in will be your body—period.
Our contract will be a strictly sexual one, with neither
of us pretending it's anything else. I thought I had made
that clear.''

Jessica clasped her hands tightly together in her lap.
The man was insufferable. She took in a deep breath
and steeled herself for battle.

''You really are a funny old duck,'' she said with a
purposely brittle laugh. ''You suggested that we embark
on a new affair, with a different set of rules from last
time...but—and do forgive me pointing this out to you—
wouldn't it be exactly as it was last time...though we
did, of course, meet more than just once a week then?
After all, you must have known I was seeing other men
at that time, and you—though you are, I'm sure, far
too gentlemanly to admit it—were seeing other women.''

She had half turned in her seat to look at Mitch as
she spoke, and felt her heartbeats give a little lurch of
alarm when she saw how pale his face had become.
Everything around her faded away abruptly and all she
was conscious of was the suddenly frozen set of his lean
features and the sensation that he had stopped breathing,
that although the Jeep was still bouncing its bone-shaking
way along the trail, he was no longer exerting any conscious control over the rugged vehicle. And then, just
when she realized she had been holding her own breath,
she heard his hiss out, and, after swallowing to relieve
the tight ache in her throat, she let the air drift silently
from her own lungs.

''Jessica Gray.'' He didn't look at her, and she saw that his face was harshly carved into a grim mask. ''You really are a first-class bitch.''

Jessica drew on all her self-control. ''I am, aren't I?'' she said, a taunting edge to her tone. ''But then, you've known that for some time, haven't you?''

Mitch rammed his foot down on the accelerator, and there was no doubt in Jessica's mind now that he knew exactly what he was doing. He was using the Jeep to give vent to his anger and his frustration. It rattled and bounced, and jumped and dove, until she thought her every bone was going to be broken, but through it all she gritted her teeth, knowing the punishment couldn't last forever. And in the end, just when she was about to scream at him to slow down, they turned a corner, the Jeep leapt out of the shadows into the sunshine again, and the vehicle's wheels dug viciously into a patch of sand-rimed grass as Mitch slammed his foot onto the brake.

Jessica's breath came out in a deep shudder, and for a long moment she just sat there, the sound of the engine gradually fading away to make room for the liquid cry of the birds swooping over the pale sand ahead, and for the splash of the frothy waves dancing at the edge of the ocean beyond.

How could it have come to this? she wondered, squeezing back a tear that ached to be set free. How could she ever have believed that she and this man were meant for each other?

Mitch had an admirable ability to regain control of his emotions and—with remarkable swiftness—to conceal them. Jessica already knew that and now he presented her with further proof of this aspect of his character. He gathered up a blanket and picnic hamper from the back seat, and by the time he'd rounded the front of the Jeep to open her door, there was nothing

in his demeanor that even *hinted* at the explosive rage
to which he'd given vent moments before.

She, unfortunately, had no such ability. She could feel
her lips tremble, could sense that her face was as bleached
of color as the fine grains of sand on the beach. Moving
stiffly beside him as they walked away from the Jeep,
she was acutely aware of the unsteadiness of her
breathing, the agitated rise and fall of her breasts as she
tried, desperately, to hide her distress. She *had* to hide
it, she knew—she had to convince Mitch she was what
he thought she was: a first-class bitch. And to convince
him of that, she had to make him believe his outburst
had left her unmoved.

Throwing him a glance from beneath her lashes, she
made to toss her bag down onto the sand, and said, with
forced brightness, "How about here?"

"No, a bit farther along." Perhaps taking his cue from
her, he used a similar nonhostile tone, and Jessica felt
some of her tension begin to dissipate.

The sand was light as sifted cake flour, and with each
step Jessica took, grains flicked up to tickle her calves.
The sun was blissfully warm on her bare arms and legs,
the sound of the sea—the whisper of white foam, the
splash of warm water—like the strains of some soft and
lovely melody in her ears. The air itself was crystal clear,
and there seemed to be magic in it. Jessica felt as if all
her senses were sharpened, and sharpened so acutely she
was aware of things in a way she'd never been before.
Mitch wasn't even touching her, yet she could feel her
skin prickle as if he was running his fingers over it; and
she could smell the musky scent of his body as surely as
if she were nestled in his arms with her cheek pressed to
his chest.

"Here we are."

They had rounded a corner and were now standing at
the entrance to another, sickle-shaped beach, hidden

from the road above by an outcropping of rock. Fringed with palm trees, it was, Jessica thought with a rush of pleasure, the most beautiful spot she had ever seen. And in the bay, a couple of miles away, was a small island, its white beaches and lush greenery vivid against the translucent waters.

"It's wonderful." Jessica's voice came out huskily. "And this belongs to Ben and Alison? What a perfect spot."

A perfect spot for seduction? The thought had come unbidden.

"Yes," Mitch said, "but they keep it for their own private use."

"But they allow you to use it?"

"Mmm. And the island, too." His gaze veered over the water as he spoke. "It's a great place to go when a person feels the need of privacy. There's a reef most of the way around it—just under the water—and tourists are warned to keep well clear of that particular island."

"Sounds wonderful."

"I'll take you there, if you like," he offered carelessly. "Tomorrow. Ben will give us a boat."

Deeper and deeper. She was getting in deeper and deeper. But that was why she was here, wasn't it? She stubbornly ignored all the warning bells clanging in her head and said, casually, "I'd like that. But you're sure Ben and Alison won't mind...your taking me there?" Oh, Lord, surely she could have made a better choice of words?

"No." Mitch's cynically amused tone revealed that the slip hadn't passed him. "They won't mind if I...take you...there."

Tiny muscles clenched way down in the pit of her stomach. "Good!" She looked at him brightly. "Then I'll look forward to it. You're very lucky that the

Wildings are so generous to you. You're obviously...privileged."

"Privileged?" Mitch had moved forward as he spoke, and she followed him. "That's a good word, Jessica, and in this case, an apt one. I feel very privileged."

"You've known Ben and his wife for four years, you said this morning?"

He hesitated, for just a moment, before turning around to face her. "I've known Ben only since I started coming to Starlight, but Alison and I..." His mouth twisted in a smile—a strangely mysterious smile, Jessica thought. "We go back a long way. A very long way."

Jessica couldn't stop herself. "Even longer than you and I?"

"Yes." A frown flickered over Mitch's brow as he looked down at her, and slowly he reached out and traced a finger over Jessica's upper lip. She managed not to flinch or react in any way. "Yes, even longer than you and I."

To her dismay, she felt a dull ache wrap itself around her heart. So he had known the lovely Alison for years, had perhaps even been going out with her while she herself had been involved with him. And, of course, he had been sleeping with Amanda then, too...

Abruptly she snapped her thoughts from *that* depressing path, a path that had caused her so much pain. "Do they have any family, Ben and Alison?"

"You're not really interested in Ben and Alison, are you, Jess?" Mitch's tone was cynical. "You don't have to pretend anymore...at least not with me. The only person you're interested in is your own beautiful self. So tell me..." He bent to throw out the blanket over the sand, and after dropping the picnic basket on top of it, along with his sunglasses, casually stripped off his shirt. "Tell me all about that beautiful self. How's your life unfolding these days? Everything going according to plan? Because I'm sure, my love, that you do have a plan!''

"Of course I have a plan.'' Jessica felt her eyelids quiver as Mitch stripped off his cutoffs and stood before her in his taupe swim trunks. "I have goals and what use are goals if you don't set out a plan for achieving them?''

"I can't argue with that, Jess. So let's hear more about these goals of yours. You were all set to shoot up the ladder when you worked at the Golden Chain—with your potential you should be at least a department head by now, yet you told Alison you were doing secretarial work? It doesn't make sense, someone with so much going for her...''

No, it wouldn't make sense to him...but then, he didn't know that she had a child.

She had made a conscious decision, when Jason was born, that he would always come first...he would always come before her career. When she had been with the Golden Chain, she had willingly, eagerly, worked many hours of overtime, both in the evening and on weekends, throwing herself wholeheartedly into her job. She knew that if she continued to do that after her baby was born, the child would lose out. So when she had applied for a position with Eric Trenton's company, she had lowered her sights and said she wanted a nine-to-five job, a job she could leave behind her when she went home at night. Because she had been ambitious, it had been a sacrifice...but one she had never regretted.

"I'm on holiday, Mitch.'' Jessica opened the button securing the waistband of her skirt, pulled down the zipper, and scooped the skirt off. She dropped it beside her sunglasses. Not quite meeting Mitch's eyes, she went on, "You heard me tell Ben I didn't want to talk about work...or even think about it...while I'm here. Do you mind...?''

She tugged up the hem of her T-shirt, and in the brief glimpse she got of his face just before she pulled the light garment over her head, she saw that Mitch's gaze had dropped to her legs. Good, she thought grimly, that's a start.

A moment later her T-shirt was lying atop her skirt, and though Jessica could feel tension clench again in her every nerve, her every muscle, she somehow managed to stretch her arms above her head in a long, lazy gesture, like a cat who has just come out from cool shadows into drowsy warmth. "Mmm," she sighed, "this is heavenly."

Without waiting for Mitch to respond, she sauntered away along the beach...and noticed, with a sinking feeling, that the Sumo wrestlers had begun to stir once more. With a sigh, she pressed the flat of one hand against her stomach. She was not, she decided tautly, cut out to play the femme fatale. It was one thing to drape her body in an alluring swimsuit, a swimsuit cut to tantalize; it was quite another to flaunt that body in a way that was designed to make Mitch burn with desire. Teasing any man was a dangerous game, but teasing a man like Mitch Carradine was tantamount to waving a red rag before a bull—

"You look different, Jessica."

She hadn't heard him come up behind her. Turning her head sharply, she found him taking his place by her side. She kept walking.

"Different? In what way?" she threw up at him coolly.

He slowed his stride to keep pace with her easy steps. "It's hard to pin down, but there seems to be a subtle change in your figure—you will forgive me, I hope, for looking at it, but it seemed, actually, as if you were wanting me to."

Did the man have invisible antennae? "Mitch, darling." She spoke in a tone that was lightly reproachful but gave no sign of her very real irritation.

"You are the one who invited me to go for a swim. You are the one who chose this isolated beach. And you're implying that I'm the one who wants something? I thought you got the message four years ago... but since you didn't, let me deliver it one last time. I want nothing from you, Mitch." She averted her face quickly just in case he caught a glimpse of the naked truth in her eyes. She did want something from him, something that was of the utmost importance to her; something that would protect her, and would assure her that Eric Trenton would never tell Mitch that she had borne his child—

"But it's not only that your hips have become more rounded, your breasts more lush and more... womanly, there's something different about the way you move. Before, there was always a certain nervous restlessness about the way you walked. Now you go forward like a woman who's been places and knows exactly where she's heading. Have you been places, Jessica," he continued softly, "since last we met?"

Oh, yes, she'd been places. But how could she tell him? He was the last person she could tell. She had been to hell and back since last they met. Months of hell, during which time—like some movie soundtrack playing over and over and over again—she had heard Amanda's voice, and then Mitch's, drifting to her disbelieving ears as she had, on her own, explored the heated greenhouse at Stokely Manor.

"...I thought Garth would be able to handle it, Mitch, but he can't. It's eating at him, making him—"

"Would it help if I were to talk to him, Mandy? I might be able to convince him that once the baby's born, he'll think differently about it, feel differently—"

"No, it won't do any good. Might even make matters worse." Amanda's voice was dull with despair. "And I can understand how he feels. Because, after all—let's not try to pretty up the facts—the child I'm carrying *is* yours.''

''I'm not denying that, but—''

Jessica shuddered inside as she recalled how she had pressed her fist to her mouth to stifle her horrified gasp, and shuddered again as she recalled how she had cringed back among the perfumed orchids, her eyes wide and disbelieving and almost blinded by tears, as Mitch and Amanda walked by, just feet from where she was standing. He had his arm around her, cradling her against his tall figure...and he was brushing a kiss over her hair, soothingly.

''Oh, Mitch, what are we going to do?'' Amanda's voice was just a whisper. ''I never guessed it would turn out this way. The last thing I wanted was for Garth to be hurt...''

''We can't go back and change the past. What's done is done, and we'll all have to live with it.'' Mitch's tone had a grim edge. ''Best thing for me to do is remove myself from the picture—at least temporarily. Perhaps that way, in time, Garth will be able to look on the child as his...''

Their voices became unintelligible, and within moments, Jessica heard the greenhouse door close behind them...and she was left standing there, tears rolling down her cheeks, her heart feeling as if it had splintered in a million bleeding pieces...

She never did know how long she stood there, shivering, in that shocked state after Mitch and Amanda left, but what she did know, and with bitter certainty, was that for the rest of her life, the scent of orchids would bring back memories of that darkest of all dark moments—

''Jessica?'' Mitch's voice came to her through what seemed like a thick wall of pain. ''Are you still with me? I asked you...have you been places since we last met?''

CHAPTER FIVE

"Mitch, you ask altogether too many questions!" Jessica drew on every ounce of her self-control to keep her distress from revealing itself in her voice. "Besides, the sun has frazzled my brain, and I'm absolutely incapable of coming up with any sensible answers. Race you to the water."

And with that, she was gone, running across the hard-packed sand, the perfect ripples left by the outgoing tide jutting up into her soles with each step, but she ignored the pain. Once in the water, once past the shallows, she felt the waves dragging against her thighs, and only then did she spear forward in a low dive. Wanting to get as far from Mitch as possible, she immediately thrust out with strong strokes, concentrating on nothing but her breathing, the sound of her arms slicing the water, and the barely audible splash of her feet kicking out behind her.

It was, of course, too good to last. Mitch was a much more powerful swimmer than she and he soon caught up with her, and could easily have outstripped her, but he didn't. He swam alongside her, almost lazily, but made no attempt to start a conversation, and after a few minutes, she flipped around and swam back toward the beach, not slowing up till she found herself in the shallows again.

Breathlessly, she surged to her feet, and, half stumbling, made her way up the gentle slope, wringing the water from the ends of her sodden ponytail as she did. The sand clung to her feet and ankles, and by the time she reached the blanket, it had scattered up over her calves. She sensed that Mitch was right behind her, and with her heart thumping, she tugged her towel from her beach bag.

As she did, her mind was racing. Should she lie on the towel, facedown, with an appearance of modesty? Or should she lie on her back, in a position that Mitch would more than likely construe as being seductive and inviting? With a feeling akin to panic, she decided to do neither. Sinking down on the towel, she sat with her legs drawn close to her body, her arms looped around her knees—for all the world, she reflected self-deprecatorily, like a wistful schoolgirl.

Mitch was standing so close that if she swayed slightly to her right, her shoulder would brush against his leg. Naked flesh to naked flesh.

She shivered.

"You're cold?"

"In this heat?" Jessica shook her head. "Lord, no." What a useless thing she was, she chastised herself. No way was she going to get any information from him if she just sat there like a lump. Taking in a deep breath, she reached both hands behind her head and slipped her ponytail free of the band securing it. Then she fanned out her wet hair and shook it so it fell in heavy strands down her back.

"Do you have a hairbrush in that bag?" Mitch asked.

"Yes, why?"

"Let me have it."

Jessica handed him her brush, feeling suddenly as if her heart had swelled so it was too big for her chest. He was going to brush her hair, untangle the knots, as he had so often done during that one summer they'd had together...

Her mouth became dry as he sat down behind her and, stretching out his long legs on either side of her, captured her in the open angle of his limbs. Her arms were no longer loosely knotted around her knees, but gripped tightly—a telltale sign of her tension that Mitch would surely notice. With an effort, she relaxed her arms, and then tried to steady her heartbeats, but without success.

Mitch seemed to be totally unaffected by their close proximity. She could hear his even breathing, could feel his breath fanning her neck as he lifted her hair and gently brushed the ends, untangling any knots. He wasn't touching her anywhere else—his legs were slightly bent at the knees, and he'd allowed them to fall open.

"It'll soon dry," he murmured, "in the sun."

Her hair was no longer knotted; she could tell by the way he was now drawing the brush from crown to tips, with the back of his free hand spread out under the silky strands so the natural bristles wouldn't scrape her shoulders. She sensed his attention was focused on what he was doing, could sense his gaze following the sweep of the brush . . .

And she also sensed the exact moment when his attention shifted from what he was doing to the body cradled, though without contact, by his own. She heard the almost imperceptible change in his breathing, heard it go from being shallow and steady to being deeper, and slightly ragged. Heard him drop the brush onto the blanket.

This was the moment, she told herself . . . and felt a wild scattering of her sensible thoughts . . . when he would make his move. This was the moment when he would put his arms around her, pull her back into his embrace, and caress the vulnerable skin at her nape with his kisses.

"Are you . . . hungry?" His voice was husky.

She knew exactly the kind of hunger to which he was referring, and, while she schooled her features so that none of her contempt for him would show, she had to admit to the relief floating through her . . . relief that he did still hunger for her body. That was his weakness, and one she would have to play on, to achieve her goal. Letting her lips curl into a languorous smile, she murmured a lazy, ''Yes, I am, actually. Starving.''

For the longest moment they stayed as they were, as if frozen in time. He, enclosing her with his body; she, dangerously balanced on a quivering thread of expectation.

And then he moved. But not in the direction she'd imagined. With a lightness surprising in a man of his size, he sprang to his feet and rubbed his hands together briskly.

''Good,'' he said. ''Then let's eat.''

Feeling disorientated, Jessica looked around with a bewildered frown...and saw that he was flicking open the lid of the small picnic hamper.

'''A jug of wine, a loaf of bread...' and a selection of cheeses, followed by Alain's own fabulous white chocolate mousse with strawberry sauce, and a flask of perfect coffee.'' Mitch raised his head and grinned at Jessica, but though his teeth gleamed pearl-bright against his dark tan, in his eyes there was no smile. Though fan lines crinkled from the outer corners, there was no twinkle of amusement in the dark gold depths; what she saw there was something quite different. A glint of mockery. Oh, it was gone in an instant, but not before she had seen it. Resentment fermented inside her. So...he had just been playing with her. He had *intended* her to believe he was coming on to her, when he had no designs on her at all.

And she had fallen right into his trap.

What kind of a game was this they had fallen into? She had not expected that she would be mouse to his cat; she had planned that it be the other way around. Still, she had one huge advantage: Mitch believed her presence on Starlight was pure chance.

But despite that advantage, he had still won this round. She stifled an irritated sigh. How she hated mind games...she had never been any good at them, had never wanted to be any good at them. Mitch had spoken the truth when he'd said earlier that she had been easy to read in the past, and that he had been expert at divining her thoughts: Was it hopeless, this mission on which she'd been sent? Was she going to leave Starlight at the end of her stay not knowing what she needed to know?

The possibility appalled her, and made her straighten her spine. Getting to her feet, she strolled across to where Mitch was standing with a bottle of wine in one hand, working out the cork with a corkscrew.

"Here," she said as the cork finally popped out, "let me get the glasses." She turned her back on him and bent over the picnic hamper with her legs straight and slightly apart, and, swaying her bottom a little, took her sweet time extricating the two wineglasses from the straps with which they were tucked against the inside lid of the basket.

"There," she murmured, "I have them." She allowed the left strap of her maillot to slip down over her upper arm. Straightening, she turned to face Mitch, pretending not to notice she was revealing far more of her left breast than was decorous. "Pour," she invited, and glanced up at him from under her thick, sooty lashes.

He poured, and his hand shook. The rim of the bottle clinked against the rim of the second glass, and Jessica adopted a slightly surprised expression.

"Are *you* cold?" she asked, her eyes guileless.

His mouth was no longer shaped in a smile, his eyes no longer adorned by crinkled lines of fake amusement, his gaze no longer tinged by mockery. "No," he said, and his voice was rough. "I'm not cold. I'm far from bloody cold." Mouth set grimly, he jammed the cork back into the bottle, and, taking both glasses from her, rammed the foot of each one into the sand by the edge of the blanket before grasping her by the shoulders and glaring down into her eyes.

"Whatever do you want?" Jessica said, trying to keep her voice steady.

His eyes were dark with anger . . . and with something else. "You know damned well what I want, you tantalizing little witch, and you also know damned well what you'll get if you waggle that delectable little behind of yours at me the way you did just now. I just hope you can handle—"

"Ahoy there!"

As the hearty male voice broke into Mitch's hissed warning, hailing them from the direction of the ocean, his gaze flew over her head and he dropped his hands from her arms as if she'd suddenly become a poisonous snake.

Free to move, Jessica stumbled back, swiveling around as she did, to see who had been calling to them. A large rowboat hovered in the shallows as several people splashed out into the water, laughing and jostling among themselves. Moments later, with the boat hauled up onto the beach, they waved to Mitch and Jessica, and then proceeded to ignore them. Chattering loudly, they made their way toward the far end of the beach, toward a stand of palm trees, lugging picnic paraphernalia with them.

"I thought—" Jessica fought to control the rapid rise and fall of her breasts, fought to make her voice sound light and slightly rueful "—that this was a private beach."

"It is." A nerve quivered at the base of Mitch's throat, but other than that, there was no sign that he was the least bit discomfited by the interruption. "The odd boat comes on it once in a while, though, and Ben and Alison are generous enough not to send trespassers packing."

So... he was going to act as if the sudden explosion of sexual tension between them hadn't happened. Fine. She would do the same. "They're nice... Ben and his wife." Jessica scooped up the glasses from their precarious position in the sand and after handing one to Mitch, she sank down onto the blanket and regulating her breathing in an attempt to steady her still-jolting heartbeats, took a sip of her wine. "You... admire Ben?"

"He's one of the best."

"You mentioned that you and Alison go a long way back. Had you lost touch with her?"

"Why would you assume that?"

"You mentioned that Garth was the one who discovered Starlight as a place to holiday, so I assumed that—"

"You could say that, yes, we had lost touch. In fact, though I didn't know where Alison was, she had kept tabs on me... on my whereabouts."

"Ah."

"What a wealth of meaning you manage to put into that one small sound, Jessica." Mitch's tone was ironic.

"Well, it's obvious you were the one who broke off the relationship, since you weren't interested in knowing what happened to Alison, while she—"

"Wrong." The denial snapped into the air between them. "She... Alison... was the one who opted out."

Jessica was surprised, and dismayed, by the sharp stab of pain that cut into her. "And you..." she kept her voice light "... came back when she called."

His lips tightened. "You could put it like that."

"Is there some other way to put it?"

He didn't answer, just paced away from her, and stood with his back to her, facing the ocean. From farther up the beach, drifted shrieks of laughter.

Jessica watched him, her eyes narrowed. "I saw you," she said bluntly. "You and Alison. Last night. Coming up from the beach together.'' His shoulders tautened, and his hands, which had been hanging loosely at his sides, clenched into fists. ''I was sitting in the shadows as you passed. Didn't know at first who it was . . . till I heard your voice.''

Still he didn't speak.

Hardly knowing what was driving her to go on, Jessica said, ''You . . . the two of you . . . still seem . . . taken with each other. Does . . . Ben know?''

He turned at last, and with the sun at his back, his face was in shadow. ''Just what are you implying, Jessica?''

Jessica finished her wine, and, moving casually, reached to put her empty glass in the basket before getting to her feet. She walked toward him, a soft gust of wind blowing her hair across her cheeks. She ignored it, and came to a halt right in front of him.

Challengingly, she looked up into his face, and took in a deep breath.

''You're having an affair with Alison, aren't you?'' she said. ''My God, Mitch, what an unspeakable rotter you are. You go around breaking up marriages without a qualm—''

His lips thinned cruelly. ''What an unspeakably nasty little mind you have, Jessica, dear. Nasty, suspicious, and mean. You see what you want to see, think the worst, and paint everyone in the same colors you've painted yourself.''

''Oh, come on, Mitch.'' Jessica stood up to him bravely, though she felt the edges of her heart curl up in response to the insults he'd hurled at her. ''What other explanation could there possibly be? You admit you knew her before. You admit she was the one who rejected you. You admit that when she whistled, you came running. What else could she be but your lover . . . and a married one, too? What else could that make her but an adulteress, Mitch? Come on, don't be coy—I'm old enough to hear the truth.''

She had never seen him look so cold before, nor so contemptuous and out of reach. He looked, she thought with an odd little chill in her heart, like someone who had been hurt so often that nothing could ever hurt him again.

''No, Jessica, you're not old enough to know the truth...or if you are, you're not mature enough to handle it. And even if you were, in this case the truth is none of your damned business. You want to put two and two together and come up with twenty-five, be my guest...but—'' he grasped her upper arms in a grip so hard it made her wince ''—if you ever put your filthy— and completely unfounded—accusations into words again, so help me I'll—''

She never discovered what it was he would do, for in the space of a heartbeat, he closed the space between his face and hers, and savaged her mouth in a kiss that bruised her lips against her teeth and sent shock waves from her crown to the tips of her toes. No one had ever kissed her like that before, with a ruthlessness so wild and primal it occurred to her, almost hysterically, that perhaps this was how prehistoric man had treated his woman before dragging her off, kicking and screaming, to his cave. But she didn't have time to kick, nor did she have time to scream. Mitch's scorching, punitive kiss was over even though her body still rocked from the shock of it. Panting, he released her and shoved her away from him, and then, fists settled on his hips, he looked down at her, his eyes dark with distaste. Faintly, from the group farther along the beach, floated a long, lewd wolf whistle. As the sound reached them, Jessica saw Mitch's jaw tighten.

''I think,'' he said icily, ''that we should eat now and then get the hell out of here.''

Jessica didn't speak; she knew that if she did, her words would come out in a tearful tumble. All she did was nod, digging her teeth into her lip to hide its trembling.

Oh, Lord, she thought as Mitch laid out the food, she had made a real mess of things. After this little incident, he would certainly not want to spend one more minute with her, but she *had* to spend more time with him. She *had* to find out what Eric Trenton wanted to know.

Mitch served the food in stony silence. Later, he tidied up the picnic things in stony silence, and drove back to the hotel in the same forbidding silence. And when they got to the front steps, he didn't bother to get out and open her door, didn't even bother to reach over and open it for her. He just sat there, with the engine running, his hands clenched around the steering wheel, his profile to her, and although Jessica opened her mouth to say "Thanks," she changed her mind and closed it again. She could tell, by the stark whiteness of his face, that whatever she wanted to say, he wouldn't want to hear it.

She jumped down to the ground, and as his Jeep roared away with an angry snarl, she watched it through eyes that were almost blinded by tears. How had she ever landed herself in this situation? she wondered despairingly.

And however was she going to get herself out of it?

The phone rang in her room that evening, just as she was about to have a shower before dressing for dinner. Wrapping a towel around herself, she hurried out of the bathroom and crossed to pick up the handset.

"Jessica?" It was Antonia...and she sounded harassed.

"What's wrong, Tonia?" That was all she needed, Jessica reflected with a feeling of panic—to find out that something was wrong at the other end, too, that perhaps Jason was ill. Her fingers tightened around the phone.

"It's...it's Eric Trenton. He...came by today—"

"Trenton? What the devil did he *want*?"

"Jess—" Antonia couldn't keep the distress from her voice "—he brought something for Jason."

Jessica put a hand to her throat. "Go on."

There was a slight hesitation, and then Antonia said miserably, "He...brought Jason a bike. A new one—top of the line. Must have cost him the earth. Jessie," she rushed on, breaking in on Jessica's enraged outburst, "there was nothing I could do. He brought the bike in—pushed his way past me—and wouldn't take it away again. Jason, of course, was thrilled to pieces."

Jessica sank down onto the bed, feeling as if her legs were going to give way. "He's just reminding me," she whispered dully, "that if he tells Mitch about Jason, this is the kind of thing Mitch will do. He'll take control, and there's nothing I can do about it...the power is with the one who has the money."

A few minutes later, after she and Antonia had finished talking, Jessica put down the phone and then brushed the tears from her eyes. What a day it had been.

Getting up slowly, she made her way back to the bathroom, and, dropping the towel distractedly, she stepped into the shower. As the hot spray stung her skin, she let her mind veer away from the news Antonia had passed on, back to her afternoon with Mitch on the beach.

Despite the steamy heat in the shower, she found herself shuddering as she recalled the grim, disgusted look on his face when she'd accused him of committing adultery with Alison...and she wondered if it was possible he'd been telling the truth when he'd denied it. That there had been *something* between them in the past, he had not denied; but whatever was going on between them now was not, apparently, an affair. Jessica muttered a frustrated exclamation. Why was it, she wondered confusedly, that she found herself, in this instance, wanting to believe Mitch? Was it because she had met Alison, and liked her, and had felt instinctively that what Alison and Ben had together was something very fine, something Alison would never betray, nor even want to betray? They had seemed so...*right*...together.

Jessica sighed as she turned off the shower taps and stepped out onto the bath mat. Whether or not Mitch had been telling the truth didn't really matter; what did matter now was that she had to screw up her courage and apologize. After what Antonia had told her about Eric's latest move, she felt an even more desperate sense of urgency than she had felt before. She had to get back on speaking terms with Mitch, and she had to do it without delay.

Frowning as she toweled herself dry, she wondered how she should approach him. The answer, though, was obvious—she would have to go to his chalet and seek him out. If he was there, she'd say she had to talk with him right away.

Would he agree? Or would he still be so disgusted with her that he'd tell her to get lost?

He *had* to agree. It was imperative that she make some sort of peace with him, at least on the surface, otherwise how was she ever going to get the information she needed?

And time was of the essence.

CHAPTER SIX

WITH her heart beating against her throat, Jessica took the lift down to the inn's foyer, and then made her way outside.

As she walked along the narrow, flower-banked path leading to Mitch's cabin, she glanced down at her outfit—a black silk shirt with black-and-silver silk trousers, and a black-and-silver braided belt to draw the two together—and hoped it was just the right thing for the occasion. The right thing for the delivery of an apology.

Her high-heeled sandals clicked noisily on the path as she approached the chalet's closed door, and she felt every muscle in her body tense in nervous anticipation. Could she go through with this? she asked herself despairingly. With each movement she made, she could feel the luxurious slither of silk against her breasts and belly, since she had nothing under her clothes but her panties—a sleek triangle of sheer black lace . . . and, of course, her perfume, which she had applied with careful frugality, so that the heat of her skin brought out only a hint of the sensual fragrance. The impression she intended to make on Mitch when he opened his door was one of touch-me-not sophistication—which was why she had wound her hair back into an intricate coil. But after the apology, if things progressed as she hoped, she would gradually reveal that below the veneer of formality was—

Her breath caught in her throat as the door opened and Mitch appeared. He stopped short at sight of her, and for a fraction of a second their eyes locked and she could have sworn she saw in his a look of blank bedazzlement, before dark shutters went up to mask his emotions.

"Mitch." She tried to make her voice calm. "I see you're going out, but can you spare me a minute?"

His eyes moved then, flickering over her, and she saw his features tighten. She knew what he was seeing, knew that her outfit was stunning, knew that her makeup—the slate gray eyeshadow, muted blush, and vibrant scarlet lipstick—completed a picture that would have turned heads anywhere, and she had to squash an involuntary rush of heady excitement and force her thoughts into a sane and logical pattern. The *only* reason she should be glad Mitch found her attractive was because this weakness in him should make it easier for her to trick him... and if she found *him* attractive—which she admittedly did, with his stark white shirt and striped tie, and narrow dark trousers—then that was a problem she would just have to deal with.

He moved toward her, leaving the door ajar. "I was just going across to the reception desk," he said curtly, "but I'll be right back." He made an abrupt gesture toward a bench under one of the windows. "Make yourself at home."

As he brushed past her, she smelled the familiar scent of his after-shave, and the clean scent of freshly laundered clothes. For a moment, he was so close she could have put her arms around his waist... and her desire to do so was so fierce it hit her like a punch in the gut. Stifling a gasp, she stumbled back as if he'd struck her. Thankfully, he had by that time gone by, and didn't see her reaction, could have had no idea of the wild emotions he'd stimulated in her. Blowing out an incredulous breath, she moved unsteadily toward the door, and leaned weakly against the jamb. This was going to be more difficult than she'd expected; she'd forgotten how vulnerable she was, had always been, to his sexual magnetism. Her heart— Dear Lord, she could hear it, tat-tat-tatting away like a thing demented.

It was only as her head began to clear that she realized it wasn't only her heart she was hearing...another similar sound was coming from inside the cabin, behind her.

And as she straightened, she became aware, with a suddenness that made her freeze where she stood, that what she was hearing was the sound of a printer.

A faxed message was coming in for Mitch.

Oh, my Lord, what an opportunity to—
No!

It was her conscience automatically rejecting what her brain was suggesting. No, there was no way she could go in there while Mitch was away and sneak a look at the message, *steal* a look at the message. That kind of behavior was anathema to her. Sneaking, stealing, cheating—

Cheating. Wasn't that what Mitch had done to her? Hadn't he cheated on her, when he had slept with Amanda, when he had impregnated Amanda with his seed while he was all the time deeply involved with her, Jessica?

It was incredible how the pain she'd felt on that day of discovery could sometimes stab at her just as agonizingly as it had then, though it was years since it had happened. But now, at this moment, she felt it twist her heart, with hard cruel fingers, till she winced from the anguish of it.

And hardly knowing what she was doing, she turned and pushed the door open and followed the sound of the printer.

It led her to what was obviously the main room of the chalet, but Jessica spared no more than a glance for the low-slung couches and chairs, the pale floor, the bright rugs and cushions that were splashes of vivid color against the cream walls. Her ears led her to an alcove to her left, and there her gaze veered like a magnet to the state-of-the-art computer and fax machine set up on a mahogany desk.

Spewing from that fax machine was paper, white paper lined with words.

Feeling as if her heart was trying to escape the boundaries of its ribbed cage, Jessica scrabbled in her bag and took out a pen. She didn't have anything to write on, but that problem was easily solved. In a wastebasket under the table were several discarded pages.

Clumsily, she snatched one up, and then leaned over the fax machine, which was still spinning out reams of words.

They were hard to read—

Well, no wonder, she was looking at them upside down!

Jessica muttered exasperatedly, and moved quickly around the end of the table so she could get a better—

"*Jessica?*"

Mitch's terse voice came from outside, through the open doorway, and as Jessica heard it, she felt the color drain from her cheeks. She whirled around, her pen slipping from her suddenly nerveless hands, to clatter on the bare floor. Stifling a cry of panic, she stuffed the scrap paper back into the wastebasket, but though she bent over and searched frantically for the pen, she couldn't see it. Had it rolled under the—?

"*Jessica?*" Mitch's voice was closer, louder... and, it seemed to Jessica's guilty mind, threaded with suspicion. The printer, she noticed distractedly, had now halted.

She glanced around desperately for another way out, and saw an open doorway leading to the kitchen. She sped through on tiptoes, and hurried to the sink. Twisting on the cold tap, she snatched down a tall glass from an open shelf and was filling it with water, when, from the

corner of her eye, she saw the shadow of Mitch's figure
as he came in from outside and crossed the main room.

"Mitch?" she called casually, and marveled that her
thumping heartbeats didn't make her voice vibrate like
a jackhammer. "I'm through here, in the—oh, you're
there!" There was just the right amount of careless surprise in her tone as she turned her head and let her eyes
meet his as she saw him standing in the kitchen doorway.
She grimaced. "I had this awful tickle in my throat.
Hope you don't mind—you did say make myself at
home."

Their gazes locked for a long moment, some kind of
tension sparking instantaneously between them. Jessica's
heartbeats still bumped against her ribs in a ponderous,
erratic way that filled her with alarm as she waited for
him to throw a suspicious glance toward the alcove...but
he didn't. He kept his gaze fixed on her.

"Have you eaten dinner?" he asked.

"Dinner?" Astonished by the question, and still
shaken by her narrow escape, Jessica stared at him
blankly. "No, I haven't. Not yet—"

"Then I'll order room service and we can eat here.
Unless you have other plans?"

"Why on earth would you want to eat with me? I
thought, after this afternoon—"

"You've come to apologize, haven't you?" Mitch
lifted his shoulders in a shrug. "I was going to look for
you with the intention of doing the same thing—"

"You *were*?"

His grin was wry. "Mmm. Only I planned to go into
the bar for a couple of drinks first."

"Dutch courage?" Jessica raised a mocking eyebrow.

"No, to deaden the part of my brain that was telling
me to keep clear of you." His grin faded, and his eyes
became serious. "But the other part of my brain was
telling me that sexual assault, no matter the provo-

cation—and I think you gave me plenty—is not an acceptable way of responding to any situation.''

He was right about that. But what she had no intention of letting him know was that though his kiss had been unwelcome, and had taken her by surprise, it had also rocked her to the very core. ''So...'' She tilted her head, her eyes challenging. ''You're ready to apologize? Or do you still need that drink first?''

''No, I don't think I need it now...but let's go over to the bar and have one anyway. We'll have dinner here in half an hour. What would you like to eat?''

''Surprise me!'' she said lightly.

''Right.''

Mitch stepped back into the main room and lifted the phone. As he spoke to someone at the other end, giving the order, Jessica made to walk by him toward the door, but with his free hand he caught her arm, making her wait, his fingers hard and possessive, and she felt a slow, heavy heat begin pulsing through her veins.

Not for the first time, and with a feeling of something approaching fear, she acknowledged that she was playing a very dangerous game.

''So.'' Jessica toyed with the stem of her near-empty wineglass. ''Who's going to start?''

''Ladies first, isn't that the usual rule? Or has that little gallantry gone by the board in light of women's lib?''

Jessica could not have failed to notice the ironic edge to Mitch's tone when he said the word ''ladies.'' He no longer thought of her as a lady, she knew that only too well. She decided to let it pass; after all, she no longer thought of him as a gentleman.

''I'm sorry.'' She looked at him steadily. ''For having jumped to conclusions about you and Alison.''

"Apology accepted. And I want to apologize for having mauled you. And also for calling you the names I did."

Jessica gave a dry laugh. "You're apologizing for saying them, but you're not really taking them back, are you? You still think I'm mean, and vicious, and—"

"I'm apologizing for *saying* them." Mitch's voice had a harsh edge. "Isn't that enough? I'm not about to start apologizing to you—or to anyone, for that matter—for what I might be *thinking*!"

"Then I shall accept what you're offering." Jessica arranged her glass carefully on the small round woven mat on the glass table between them. "Because thoughts are private things and one should never be forced to share them." And wasn't that the truth! If Mitch could see into her mind and discover what was going on in there, he'd—

"Another glass of wine, Jessica?"

She noticed their waiter was hovering by their table, and Mitch was looking questioningly at her. Jessica opened her mouth to say, "No, thanks," but changed her mind. "Yes," she said. "Please."

The waiter refilled her glass, and Mitch's too, before leaving them alone again.

"So—" Mitch leaned back lazily in his chair "—now that we've settled the business part of the evening to our mutual satisfaction, what would you like to talk about, Jessica?"

Jessica traced a finger around the rim of her wineglass and looked up at him with an expression of what she hoped looked like nothing more than polite interest. "What's Amanda doing these days? Does she have a job?"

"No, she's not working."

"I seem to remember she had a diploma in interior design. I'm surprised she wouldn't want to put it to use."

"Oh, she will, eventually. Probably when Megan starts school. She's going to be five at Easter, and she'll be going into kindergarten at the end of August."

"Megan's her daughter?" Jessica realized suddenly that she was now holding the stem of her glass so tightly it was a wonder she hadn't snapped it. With an effort she put the glass down, drew her hand away, and twined her fingers tightly together in her lap. "Amanda's and Garth's?"

As she spoke, she kept her gaze fixed with grim intent on Mitch's face, wanting to see if his expression changed as she broached the sensitive subject. Not that he would know she was aware it was sensitive! She was probably one of the few who knew that Mitch had fathered Amanda's child.

"That's right." His gaze remained steady.

"Didn't you tell me," Jessica pressed, "that Garth had died of a hereditary heart disease? Weren't he and Amanda afraid that it would be passed on?" She threaded her tone with concern, knowing Mitch would expect that reaction. "Is the little girl...Megan...is she all right?"

"Megan?" He gave a low chuckle. "Oh, Megan's fine—healthy as a horse, actually. You see—"

"Mr. Carradine?" A dark-skinned young waiter had appeared at Mitch's elbow. "You asked me to let you know when your dinner would be ready. Alain will be sending it over to the chalet in two minutes."

"Thanks, Pete." Mitch slipped the waiter a tip, pushed his chair back, looked across at Jessica, his brows raised.

"Ready to go?" he asked.

Jessica nodded, and pushed her own chair back, all the time feeling ready to explode with frustration. While she'd been listening to Mitch, she'd felt her pulses accelerate in frantic anticipation. What was Mitch going to say? Was he going to tell her Garth wasn't Megan's father? Was he going to tell her, at last, the truth—that he and Amanda had had an affair and the child— Megan—was his? Oh, if only the waiter had arrived just one minute later, she might have heard Mitch admit everything. But why had he been ready to talk about it now? That was a total puzzle! Surely it wasn't just because Garth was dead; if the truth got out, it could still hurt Amanda—

She realized with a start that Mitch was right behind her. He lifted her purse and handed it to her, and then, with his palm in the small of her back, he edged her out of the now crowded bar... and as he did, as he touched her, awareness shivered through her and all thoughts of Amanda and Garth scattered like crisp leaves in an autumn gale.

Had he noticed that she had nothing on below her silk shirt? Jessica felt as if her brain was exploding with little silver stars. He was caressing his fingertips up and down her spine, almost absently, but she felt him stiffen as he reached the spot where a bra clasp would be... *should* be.

Even as she tried to catch her breath, which had snagged strangely, she heard him make a small, almost imperceptible sound in his throat. Slipping his hand from her back, he slid it sensually down her arm to her wrist, which he circled with his strong possessive fingers.

The electricity arcing between them should have lit up the evening as they stepped out into the summer night, a night dusky with sweet scents, and tanged by the ocean. It made Jessica feel as if she was being pulled to him by magic. She could only hope that while that magic lasted, it would work with her, and not against her....

The waiter arrived with their dinner just moments after they got back to the chalet, and his bustling presence broke the tension that had been escalating dangerously between them.

After he'd set out the food on a table by the window, chatting volubly all the time, he left with a wide grin and a friendly, "You have a good dinner, now."

It *was* a good dinner, and Jessica was surprised to find that despite her tightly strung nerves, and despite the frustration resulting from their interrupted talk, she was able to enjoy it. A piquant salad came first, and then Mitch loaded her dinner plate with chicken curry, breadfruit fritters, a serving from a delicious and un-usual banana, tomato and mango casserole, smothered in a sauce so hot she gasped as it exploded on her tongue. The dessert—homemade ice cream in a cool, mint green—happily acted as a natural fire extinguisher, and it was with a sigh of genuine pleasure that Jessica sat back in her seat after she had finished, and watched Mitch pour two cups of coffee.

"A liqueur?" He cocked a questioning brow.

"No, thanks...but you go ahead." They'd had wine with their dinner, and Jessica knew she really shouldn't have any more alcohol. She already felt dangerously light-headed, and she knew that if she made just one tiny slip, revealing things to Mitch that she didn't want him to know, then all her plans could blow up in her face.

"No, I'm fine."

His gaze was on her, his eyes dark pools of mystery. How she would have loved to be able to see way down into those pools, and discover what lay in the shadowy depths—

"So, Jess, what *have* you been up to these past years?" He swallowed a gulp of his coffee, and laid the cup down again in its saucer. "They say it's a small world, but it's not so small that a person can't disappear without trace if they want to. Were you hiding from me?" he asked, his lips curling up in a gentle smile, a smile which didn't raise one shimmer of answering light in those dark-pooled eyes.

"I thought a clean break would be best," Jessica said after an almost imperceptible hesitation. "You seemed to want more than I was prepared to give . . . of course, I didn't know then that you would have been satisfied just to have an affair," she added smoothly.

"Did I use the word satisfied?" Mitch toyed with his coffee spoon. "I don't think I did. I wouldn't have been satisfied, Jess . . . not then, I was too far gone with love to have been satisfied with that. Now, though . . ." His tone became mocking. "I'd settle for an affair. God, how much easier it is to have relationships where neither party needs nor wants strings or commitment. But you must already know that, having never gone in for any other kind."

Just for a second, when he said "I was too far gone with love" Jessica had felt her heart flame with a fire that set her blood pounding. He *had* loved her. At least, she hadn't been wrong about that. But almost instantly the fire dulled to gray embers. What did it matter if he *had* been in love with her? It was a treacherous kind of love, a love that was faithless and not worthy of the name.

"Love." She gave a cynical laugh. "Such a small word yet it's responsible for so much heartache. If people were honest, they'd use another four-letter word to describe that overrated emotion . . ."

Mitch raised his eyebrows.

"T-r-a-p." Jessica smiled, hoping she looked amused, though that was the last thing she was feeling. "Love's a trap, Mitch. And relationships shouldn't be like traps. Two people who are attracted to each other should be able to enjoy each other, without being forced into a

situation they don't want to be in. People aren't posses-
sions—''

Mitch gestured with open hands, expressing
agreement. ''You don't have to argue that point with
me, not anymore. I'm a convert—and an enthusiastic
one to boot! Love is a word that never passes my lips
now...at least not when I'm trying to seduce a woman.
At any rate, I've found it's unnecessary. The opposite
sex seem delighted to walk into my...trap...without
any promises of undying love on my part. Aren't you
proud of me?'' He smiled, and at last his smile reached
his eyes, so that they sparkled.

And he looked in that moment so like Jason that
Jessica felt her heart contract with panic. Jason. She
might lose him, if she didn't succeed in her mission. Dear
heaven, Mitch was such a charmer—and he was already
charming her out of remembering why she was here. *She
had to find out what was on that fax message that had
come in earlier.*

''Yes,'' she said mockingly, ''I'm very proud of you.''
She got to her feet, and went on casually, ''May I use
your washroom?''

''Go ahead.'' Mitch stood up. ''Just past that alcove.''

As she walked past the alcove, she noted in a swift
sideways glance that the papers were still lying by the
fax machine; and then she looked down, feeling furtive
and nervous, hoping to catch sight of her pen somewhere on the floor, but it was nowhere to be seen.

Once in the bathroom, she closed the door and leaned
back against it, feeling her heart pounding as hard as if
she'd been running for miles. What could she do to dis-
tract Mitch? It was possible she'd never be invited back
into the chalet again, so she *had* to take this one chance
to see what was on those papers.

A few minutes later, with her lipstick refreshed and a
faint misting of perfume in her hair, she emerged from

the bathroom. She felt her heart give a lurch as she saw Mitch standing in the alcove, gathering up the loose sheets of paper, and patting them into a neat pile. He glanced around at her, saying absently, "I should have locked these away earlier. I'll do it now—it'll just take a sec."

Lock them away. Jessica felt a wild surge of panic. Once the papers were locked away, unless she could persuade Mitch to talk, she'd never find out his plans. Even as she smiled back at him serenely, and walked toward him, her mind was racing frantically around, trying to decide what she should do. But as she made to pass by him, one of the papers fluttered from the pile and floated to the floor in front of her. Throat aching as if someone was tightening a rope around her neck, she swiftly bent and scooped the paper up and then stepped away backward, into the main room. Holding out the paper teasingly, she waved it in the air. "Here," she challenged with a chuckle, "come and get it."

He made an impatient gesture. "Give it, Jess."

"Uh-uh." She retreated, till she felt her calves bump a piece of furniture. "If it's so very important, I might just keep it."

He began to walk toward her, and he looked big and threatening . . . and very, very dangerous.

Jessica swished the paper behind her back.

He stopped in front of her, so close she could almost feel the heat of his body against her own. His breath was fragrant with coffee and wine; his hands, as they brushed against her in his effort to reach behind her, hard and warm against her ribs.

She arched back, but he was not about to give up; she heard the whisper of silk as his body aggressively brushed the tips of her breasts.

"Jessica." His voice had a slight rasp, a very sexy rasp. "You're asking for trouble."

She looked up into his face and realized, with a thrill of nervous excitement, that he was no longer interested in retrieving the sheet of paper. His gaze was clouded, his lips slightly parted, his breathing ragged.

She felt her fingers slacken, and heard, in a distant part of her mind, a rustle as the paper fluttered to the floor. Mitch's arms were around her, he was drawing her up into him, and his lips were just inches away from her own.

"Sensual witch!" he muttered. "You are one sensual little witch."

His kiss was an explosion of sensation, his closeness a starburst of pleasure. Thoughts of faxes, and secrets, and seduction to order, no longer had a place in her brain. All she could think of was that whatever had existed between them five years before was still there, and was still powerful enough to melt away her desperate determination to resist; she was as helpless in his arms as—

"You're sensational in black silk, Jessie." His lips were dancing kisses across her jaw, his hands doing a slow waltz down her back. "You know how to arouse a man, don't you? Black silk on milk-white skin. My God, what a lethal combination. Tell me, sweet Jess... why didn't you wear a bra tonight?"

With a supreme effort, Jessica focused her mind on the part she was supposed to be playing. "Because..." she brushed a kiss against his throat, and her voice was deliberately husky, deliberately seductive, as she went on "... when I dressed, I was thinking about you..."

She felt his arms tighten around her, and he pulled her even closer to him. "Do you know how damned tantalizing it is," he growled roughly, "to sit across someone at dinner, knowing that under black silk there's nothing to conceal beautiful breasts...?"

Jessica shuddered, and she knew he had felt it . . . and she knew, too, that she was perilously close to falling under his spell . . . and if she allowed that to happen, she would no longer be acting the part of a woman wanting to be seduced, but living that part . . . and, Lord forgive her, enjoying it.

"The past hour has been like an eternity, Jessie, waiting for this moment." Mitch's voice had become thick with passion. "But there's nothing to whet a man's appetite like having to wait. The anticipation is half the pleasure."

She swallowed painfully as Mitch caressed the curve of her hip, the indentation of her waist, the delicate ripple of her ribs.

"Take down your hair." The command came in a congested whisper.

Like a slave, she raised her arms, fumbled with the clasp, dropped it uncaringly. Breasts arched up to him, she untwisted the heavy glossy coil, and with her trembling fingers weaving through the thick swinging mass, she let it fall around her shoulders and down her back.

His lips were on hers again, his fingers working with the buttons of her blouse. In seconds he had opened each tiny black pearl disc, in seconds he had slipped the garment over her shoulders. It fell, she heard it fall, in a provocative slither, to the floor.

Naked. She was naked now from the waist. And his hands, those clever hands, had undone the button at the waist of her silver-and-black trousers, and the garment slid to the floor to settle atop her blouse.

"God . . ." His hands were shaking as he encountered the lace bikini panties, and his voice shook, too, as he said, in almost a groan, "You're too much, Jessica . . . almost more than a man can handle."

But he could handle her. She felt light as a summer breeze as he carried her through to his bedroom, and as cherished as a priceless piece of Meissen as he lowered her to his bed. She lay back, giving herself to him with an almost anguished ecstasy as he knelt by the bed and paid the most intimate and reverent homage to her body.

It was only when he had reduced her to a mindless state of desperation that he finally surrendered to her incoherent begging. He lay back on the bed, and pulled her over him, so that her hair, in the moonlight, looked like a shimmer of black satin. He buried his face in the scented cascade, as if he could die with the wonder of it, and only when she finally sought his lips in a passionate hunger that demanded to be appeased, did he at last give her what she wanted.

What she needed.

What they both needed.

They had made love before, many times during their affair, but never with such intensity, and never with such aching tenderness. And in another way their lovemaking was different. They had been apart for more than four years, so there was a breathless newness in their coming together . . . but mingled with that special excitement was their old familiarity with each other's bodies . . .

With each other's vulnerabilities.

Oh, they knew so well how to give each other pleasure, it was a knowledge that would be with them forever. And they both used that intimate knowledge to the full, bringing each other to spiraling heights over and over again, before finally, in a moment of ecstasy so explosive Jessica felt as if she was trembling on the edge of delirium, they reached the zenith of fulfillment together.

As they lay satiated in each other's arms, with Mitch's warm breath fanning her tousled hair, and his chest rising and falling against her own, Jessica felt tears wetting her cheeks.

And tears spilling from her heart.

She had set out to betray, but she had betrayed only herself, for she knew now, that no matter how contemptibly Mitch had behaved toward her in the past, she was still in love with him.

And would be till the day she died.

CHAPTER SEVEN

"JUST like old times, isn't it, Jess?"

Jessica opened her eyes, and blinked as early morning sunlight dazzled her. Mitch had one elbow on his pillow, and he was looking down at her, his thick brown hair tousled from sleep. As he moved his head toward her, it blotted out the bright rays and she could see his face more clearly. He was, she saw, smiling, his eyes lazy and warm . . . and his fingers were gentle as he brushed back the thick strands of glossy black hair that had fallen over her cheek.

She felt as if her heart was breaking, all over again. But that was something he would never know. Must never know.

"Yes." She tilted her head back on her pillow and looked up at him. "It was just like old times . . ." Her lips curled in a purely feminine smile. "Only better."

"Must you go home today, Jess?"

Jessica closed her eyes, lest he see any sign of the anxiety mirrored there. Home. She had to get home, before Eric Trenton did any more damage—

"Jess?" Mitch's lips touched her brow, and she felt the roughness of his unshaved jaw on her skin. "Do you?"

"Yes." Her tone was husky. "I'm afraid so."

"But we'll see each other again—"

She touched a fingertip to his lips, stopping him. "No commitments, no promises, remember?" Trailing her nail across his lower lip, she blinked back threatening tears and forced a smile. "Let's make the most of today, and let tomorrow take care of itself."

She thought she saw a shadow cross his eyes, but a second later it was gone. "If that's what you want."

"It is ..."

"Then—" he lowered his mouth to hers, his eyes cloudy with desire "—let's not waste one precious minute."

This time when Mitch kissed her, she kept her brain alert ... something she had not managed to do the previous night, when she had given herself mindlessly to his lovemaking. This time, she forced herself to control that part of her that wanted to float dazedly into a world where nothing existed but the passion flaming between them. She had to think ... she had to decide what she was going to do. Mitch would, she was sure, fall asleep again after they made love, perhaps for just a short while, but it would be long enough. Long enough for her to find that sheet of paper that had fluttered to the floor the night before, long enough for her to skim a searching look over it ... long enough for her to find the information she needed ...

His lips were pressing urgent kisses along her neck, on the sensitive spot just under her ear. Twisting her head, she managed to snatch a glance at her watch, and saw that she still had over nine hours before she left the island.

His hands were pushing back the sheet, his palms skimming over her ribs, teasing, tantalizing, drawing the breath from her lungs. Knowing there was nothing she could do now, nothing she could do till later, Jessica closed her eyes and twined her fingers more tightly into his hair, and gave in to the waves of pleasure already invading her body.

*   *   *

The paper was lying on the rug, just where it had fallen when it had fluttered from her trembling fingers.

Jessica tiptoed across the floor toward it, her teeth dug into her lower lip, every nerve in her body screaming in silent tension. From the bedroom she could hear the sound of rhythmic snoring, and an image floated into her mind, an image of Mitch lying sprawled across the bed—almost naked but for the sheet trailing around his thighs—as he had been when she'd darted a swift glance back into the room before sneaking so furtively away. The image was vivid, and had the power to melt every bone in her traitorous body...

Drawing in her breath, she bent to scoop up the paper, grasping it carefully, so it wouldn't rustle at her touch. Her head, she realized, was pounding, and she found it difficult to focus her eyes on the print...it seemed to dance, to taunt her—and then she realized it was her fingers that were shaking, not the typed words on the paper.

Re your offer to purchase the Markington Estate, this is to confirm same delivered by hand, as per your orders, to Lester Forgan's lawyer in the Regency Tower Building this morning, in the amount of...

Jessica stifled a gasp of shock...shock not untinged with awe...as she saw the incredible sum Mitch was offering for the property in question. The Markington Estate.

The estate was in Wiltshire. She remembered seeing a photograph of its magnificent manor house in a recent For Sale ad in one of the property magazines that crossed her desk in the course of her work...and she also recalled the figure to which offers had been invited, a considerable figure but yet well below the bid mentioned in this fax. No one in his right mind would offer such an astronomical price—not unless money was no object and the person was absolutely hell-bent on owning the estate, whatever the reason. And Mitch was obviously hell-bent on beating out all possible competitors; in fact, with a bid this high, he would feel absolutely confident of leaving them all at the starting gate—

The snoring had stopped.

Jessica froze for a nerve-chilling moment...and then, as she heard the gentle rhythmic sound start up once again, she exhaled a small sigh of relief. Mitch must have turned over in his sleep.

She had to get out of there.

Without a sound, she put the paper back on the floor. She had dressed earlier, the moment she'd been sure Mitch was asleep, and now she crept to the outside door, her bare feet making scarcely a sound.

The door creaked slightly as she pulled it open, but though she grimaced, she didn't wait to find out if the noise had disturbed Mitch. She fled along the path toward the side door of the inn, praying it would be unlocked. It was.

Once inside, she put on her shoes, and slowed down, concentrating on regulating her breath, which was coming in great fits and shudders.

Thankfully she didn't meet anyone on the way to her room, and once safely there, she crossed immediately to the phone. With the time difference, the Trenton Company's offices would already be open, and the sooner she told Eric Trenton what he wanted to know, the sooner she would feel as if the heavy cloud hanging over her would be lifted.

Moments later the girl at the hotel switchboard connected her with the number she wanted, and with the phone pressed closely to her ear, she heard Jane, the Trenton Company's senior secretary, say crisply, "Good morning, Trenton Property Company."

"I'd like to speak to Eric Trenton, please."

And then he was at the other end of the line. As Jessica heard his familiar voice say, "Trenton speaking," she took a second to picture him—an overweight, pompous man in a large, impressive office, where almost everything around him was stamped with the Trenton Company logo. A person to whom appearances were vitally important, Eric Trenton liked the company name to be stamped on everything in the building where possible, from the cafeteria staff's uniforms, to the coffee mugs, to the smallest eraser in the typing pool...and even on the toilet rolls in the washrooms. And everything had to be kept immaculate; as he himself was immaculate, always dapper in one of his many pin-striped suits, with his mustache neatly trimmed, his thin hair smoothly combed, and his nails neatly manicured—nothing in his appearance even hinting at the dark side he kept hidden from the world.

"It's Jessica Gray," she said in a low, hard tone.

She could almost hear the tension snapping into place between them. "Yes?" His tone was curt, but there was no mistaking the strain in his voice—a sign of the pressure he was under, in his self-imposed rivalry with Mitch.

Jessica's fingers curled around the phone, her knuckles white, as despair and self-contempt mingled inside her like a foul whirlpool. Was she really doing this? She'd never believed she was capable of doing something so underhanded, so devious...so despicable. Betrayal. Like blackmail, it was a very ugly word.

But Mitch's behavior had been ugly, too, five years before. And what she was doing, she was doing for Jason's sake. Surely, in a case like this, the ends justified the means? She had to believe that. She did believe that. She closed her eyes and swallowed the lump that had formed in her throat as if it wanted to deny her the use of her voice. ''It's—'' she slumped down on the edge of the bed ''—it's the Markington Estate.''

She heard a quick hissing sound. ''The Markington Estate. My God, of course. What a prize . . . and what a location for—'' He broke off. ''And his offer?'' he demanded harshly.

Eyes wild and desperate, Jessica looked around the room, as if looking for a way to escape. But there was no escape. She had come this far, she had to go all the way. She mumbled her response.

''For God's sake, woman, speak up!''

But even as she repeated what she'd said, clearly this time, she knew Eric had heard her the first time, knew he was just digging the knife in. And knew by the elation in his voice as he repeated the amount, that the information she'd given him had made his day.

Just as it had ruined hers.

But better that than put Mitch Carradine into a position where he could infect her son's life, she reflected with a bitter twist of her mouth.

''Thank you, Jessica, you've done well. And in return, I shall—''

''In return, all I want is for you to keep your promise.''

And with that, she hung up the phone, despite knowing how furious he'd be at the way she had thus taken control of their conversation. But she couldn't help it; she hated him, hated everything he stood for.

But one thing was sure; she would never let herself be put in the same kind of a position again. She had a hold over Eric Trenton now, just as he had had a hold over her. If he stepped out of line once, if he ever tried to use his knowledge to try to blackmail her again, she would threaten him with going to the authorities and spilling the beans about how he'd engineered the bidding on the Markington Estate. She was well aware he would never risk having that become public.

Knowing she had that power now was a consolation, though one that gave her little pleasure. But at least he no longer posed any danger to her. And once she got back home, she would start, very discreetly, looking for another job. Perhaps somewhere in Scotland. Someplace where she need never bump into Eric Trenton again...and someplace where she could hide from Mitch, in case he ever found out she was the reason he had lost the Markington Estate.

After she'd showered and washed her hair, Jessica dressed, and then made herself a pot of coffee in her room. She poured herself a cup, and drank it as she tidied her things.

The phone rang three times, but she ignored it. She hung the Do Not Disturb notice outside her door, and later, when someone knocked, and even turned the door handle, she ignored that, too. It would probably be Mitch, and she was feeling far too vulnerable to see him.

As she finished her coffee, Jessica glanced frowningly at her watch. She was scheduled to catch the five o'clock ferry, but now that she had accomplished her mission, there was no need to stay. There was an earlier ferry, one that was due to sail in about twenty minutes and if she left now, she could probably make it, and not have to spend the rest of the day trying to avoid Mitch—

But she'd have to hurry.

Without giving herself time to change her mind, she called the desk and asked for a porter to be sent up to her room in five minutes. Then she went through to the bathroom and cleaned her teeth quickly, before zipping up her sponge bag and tucking it into her case, along with the rest of her clothes. She was just locking the case when she heard a tap on the door.

"Coming," she called as she crossed the room to open the door for the porter—

But it wasn't the porter. It was Mitch who stood there, leaning against the doorjamb with a lazy smile.

Jessica felt her pulses lurch forward in panic as she stared at him. He was looking devastating in a stone-colored shirt and white shorts, and her heartbeats thudded painfully as she recalled the night of love they had just spent together. Everything in her—every uncontrolled and wanton cell in her—hungered to reach out and put her arms around him. She dug her hands into the slash pockets of her linen trousers.

"Surely you're not leaving, Jess? As I passed the desk, I thought I heard someone say you'd called for a porter." He came closer, and his familiar male scent drifted to her, tantalizingly, invitingly.

Like sweet petals exposed to sunshine, her own skin gave off an answering scent, something totally beyond her ability to control. "I've decided to take the next ferry to Guadeloupe, do some shopping and sight-seeing at Pointe-à-Pitre—I'm spending the night there and flying out early, to Antigua—my connecting flight to Gatwick is at eleven—"

"You were going to leave without saying goodbye?"

She took a deep breath. "I . . . did look for you." Liar.

"You didn't answer my calls earlier. You didn't come to your door when I knocked."

"Mitch, I—"

"The little island—I promised to borrow Ben's boat and take you there today. Come, Jess, it'll be fun." He reached out and twined a lustrous lock of her loose hair over the back of his hand, capturing it, and drew her gently toward him. His lips were only a breath away, his eyes so deep she could feel herself drowning in them. "What are you running from, sweet Jessie?"

"I'm . . . not running—"

"Last night . . ." His voice was husky, his breath tender and warm against her cheeks. "Oh, Jess, last night—"

"Last night was...one for the road, Mitch." Jessica felt her brow dew with perspiration. "Or...one for the scrapbook. Memory's scrapbook."

"We can make more memories. I want to make many, many more memories with you, sweetheart. You said you'd think about my offer. Have you...thought about it?"

Jessica felt as if his fingers were tugging desperately at her heart as she looked at the stark expression in his eyes, the lines of strain around his mouth, the rigid set of his shoulders. Did he really want to get involved with her again, in a "permanent, temporary affair"? And did he want her to stay, today, as badly as he appeared to? Oh, she must be wrong. Mitch Carradine wasn't capable of feeling any kind of deep emotion, any kind of lasting true emotion. She knew that, if she knew nothing else. And yet, at this moment, he looked as if she was putting him through the worst kind of hell.

"Oh, I'll think about it," she murmured evasively, "if it's what you really want—"

"What I really want, at this moment, is to spend the rest of today with you." The hand twined around her hair pulled her even closer. "Just one day," he urged, his voice husky with invitation, "is all I ask. One day out of time."

One day out of time...

What do you have to lose?

The treacherous voice in her head was in league with the treacherous stirrings in her heart. She might have withstood one, but how could she withstand both? Oh, not with Mitch's fingertips caressing her nape, with his body lightly, seductively brushing against hers...

"That sigh, Jess..." His voice was like warm syrup running over her skin. "It seemed to come from the depths of your soul. It's not a life or death decision, is it? To spend a few more hours with...an old friend?"

"All right." Had she really said that? "I'll stay." Yes, that was her voice. "But you'll get me back by five, so I can catch the last ferry?"

"On my honor as a Scout," he said gravely, raising his right hand in an impressive salute.

"You were never in the Scouts," she protested, but before she could say more, a porter suddenly materialized beside them.

Mitch gave him no time to speak. "Here." He slipped the man a generous tip. "Change of plan," he explained. "The lady won't be leaving this morning after all."

Smiling widely, the porter left, and as he did, Mitch glanced down at Jessica's linen trousers and silk shirt and said, "I'll give you ten minutes to get changed into something more casual while I go back to the chalet for my trunks, and order a packed lunch. And this time," he flung back over his shoulder, his eyes dark with promise, "I'll make sure we both enjoy it. See you out front in ten minutes."

What had she let herself in for? Jessica wondered dazedly as she slumped sideways against the doorjamb; and why had she let Mitch take over the way he had?

Oh, she knew the answer to the second question, knew it only too well. When he had pulled her against him, when he had teased her with his body, he had beguiled her in a way she found impossible to resist. Lily-livered. That's what she was, succumbing without a whimper to his potent sex appeal.

But as for the first question—what had she let herself in for?—time alone would come up with the answer to that.

"Here we are, Jess . . . ours for the day, thanks to Ben."

Mitch switched off the outboard motor, and as the

sound faded away, to be lost in the swish of the wavelets dancing on the shore, he jumped out into the shallows.

Jessica took off her sandals and clambered out after him, wading up the gentle slope and then slipping on her sandals again while Mitch hauled the boat out of the water. Once it was safely beached, he unloaded the picnic hamper and led the way across the white sand toward the coconut palms fringing the beach area.

''Ben built a cabin here a long time ago,'' he said as he took her along a shadowy path. ''He and Alison used it quite a bit when they were younger, though very rarely now. Once in a while, they rent it to a honeymoon couple...''

Jessica was listening to Mitch, but only with part of her mind. In the other part, the deep and emotional part, she felt a persistent niggling, as if her intuitive senses were trying to tell her things were not as they seemed.

But what could be wrong? She certainly hadn't felt that way when Mitch had come to her room to invite her out on the boat, yet when he'd picked her up, a bare ten minutes later, she'd sensed something different about his attitude. The change was so slight that had she not been so attuned to his moods, she would probably not have noticed it. And even now, she couldn't put her finger on what was wrong, what was off-key. He was talking away nonchalantly, and his manner was friendly, as it had been during the short boat trip.

On the surface.

Jessica frowned and bit her lip. Why did that warning bell keep sounding in her head? What could have happened during those brief ten minutes when they were apart? It could have nothing to do with the Markington Estate bids, because the deadline was not till tonight at twelve, and the bids would all remain sealed till then, so there was no way he could have discovered his bid had been unsuccessful.

Oh, she must be imagining things—probably because of her guilty conscience! Good Lord, she had even thought, on their way here, that Mitch's eyes had seemed icy cold on one occasion when she'd turned unexpectedly and caught him looking at her—but it must have been a trick of the light, because even as she blinked in response to the blast of hostility she thought she'd seen, he'd taken one of her hands in his and, turning it over, had brushed a casual kiss across the fine-veined skin at her wrist.

"This is it, Jess," he was saying now. "What do you think of it? Quite a hideaway, hmm?"

With a determined effort, Jessica pushed her doubts to the back of her mind as she and Mitch came out into an open area. A day out of time, he had said. That's what they were going to have, and now that she was here, in this paradise, she would be a fool not to enjoy it! Her gaze traveled delightedly over the tiny log cabin straight ahead, with its quaint thatched roof and scarred, emerald-painted wooden door. "How lovely!" She turned to Mitch impulsively. "May we go inside?"

"Of course." He took a key from the pocket of his shorts. "Here—" he handed it over "—it's all yours."

With a feeling of anticipation, Jessica stepped across to the door and after a brief struggle with the lock, opened it. Inside it was shadowy, and surprisingly cool, and as she walked forward, Mitch said from behind, "It's pretty basic. Just this room, a small bedroom, and an outdoor toilet. Kitchen facilities are minimal."

"I can see that," Jessica said wryly as she noted the dented white enamel basin set on the counter. "No plumbing? No fridge? No running water?"

Mitch threw open a small cupboard by the shuttered window. "Nothing but some cutlery and china. Can't leave fresh food lying about in this climate. Anyone using the cabin has to be self-sufficient, has to enjoy roughing it.''

''Honeymoon couples, I've heard, don't do very much cooking or entertaining,'' Jessica said.

''You'll never know, will you?'' Mitch said lightly as he dumped the hamper on the countertop. ''Since you're—''

''Never going to get married. Right. But how about you, Mitch?'' she asked archly. ''Do you think that one day you and a beautiful young bride will spend your first nights of wedded bliss here—'' she moved across to the open doorway leading to the bedroom ''—on this very bed?''

The bed wasn't very big—not quite a double, Jessica reflected, but wider than a single. Mosquito netting hung around it, to protect the occupants while they slept...or, she took in a deep breath as she sensed Mitch coming up behind her, as they made love.

''If this bed could only talk.'' His voice was amused, but the fingers he curled around her shoulder were firm and hard. ''It would have some tales to tell.''

''It's just as well it can't, then,'' Jessica countered, ''because I, for one, wouldn't want to listen.''

''But you like to eavesdrop, don't you, Jessie, dear?'' His fingers tightened on her flesh. ''You had no qualms about listening to my conversation with Alison that night on the beach?''

She jerked her shoulder free of his grip, turning abruptly to stare up at him with a flare of anger in her eyes. ''That was accidental,'' she snapped. ''I'd never purposely try to overhear—''

''Just as well,'' he said softly, ''since you have a gift for misunderstanding what you do hear, and putting the worst possible interpretation on it.''

''If you're going to be nasty and bring all that up again, we might as well call this whole thing off.''

Shoving her way past him, Jessica stormed outside, making her way back toward the beach. But before she had gone ten yards, he had caught up with her, and strode easily alongside her.

"You won't get very far on your own," he said with a chuckle, "unless you're a powerful swimmer. It's a long way to shore... and I have the only key to the outboard motor."

She stopped short, and glared up at him. "Take me back, then," she snapped. "I wish to heaven that I'd left on that early ferry as I wanted to. Why I agreed to come here with you, I don't know! I—"

"Don't you?"

The blunt question stopped her dead in her tracks. Perhaps later she would be able to come up with some snappy comment that would have put him in his place, but right now, impaled as she was in his tawny gaze, enmeshed as she was in his sexual web, she had no such repartee available. To her dismay, she felt her throat tighten, her eyes sting.

"I think we both know the answer to that question," he said simply. "But for now—I think we would be wise to leave it. Let's have a dip before lunch."

He took her by the hand and led her back to the boat, where they had left their towels and swimsuits. Jessica felt like a child on an outing—a child who'd had a tantrum, a tantrum that was not forgotten, but had been put temporarily on the back burner.

A few minutes later, however, as she splashed into the water alongside Mitch and he threw her a heart-stopping grin, she pushed any lingering anxieties to a far corner of her mind, and set out to enjoy herself.

*   *   *

After a long, lazy swim, they ate lunch under a palm tree on the beach, chatting about nothing in particular, then lingered over the last of a bottle of red wine. Only after repacking the picnic hamper with some biscuits and fruit, and half a flask of coffee—the remains of their lunch—did Mitch begin to talk in a more serious vein.

"Tell me, Jess," he said. "How are your sisters? What were their names again—Antonia, I believe . . . and Fen? Antonia was the one who lost her husband just before you and I met. What's she doing these days? Didn't she have two small children—twins?"

"Mmm—a boy and a girl. Fen's fine, still running her bookshop up in Scotland, and Tonia's doing well now, too, though she had a rough time in the beginning—she found it hard coping with Dominic and Rebecca without Tom to help. Fortunately Tom had life insurance, so at least she's had no money worries."

"Does she have a job?"

"No, but she plans to go back to teaching after the summer, when the twins start school. She's already sent in application forms to several school boards."

"And is there a man in her life?"

Jessica smiled wryly. "I'm afraid not." Her smile faded and she gathered up a handful of sand, and with a thoughtful frown, let it sift through her fingers. "It's a bit of a worry to me, actually—the way she won't let go of the past. Oh, I know Tom was wonderful, and he was so good to her, but . . ."

"Memories don't keep you warm on a winter's night, or something like that." Mitch's voice was quiet. "So, she doesn't date, doesn't go out with men at all?"

Jessica shook her head. "No, she just smiles that charming smile of hers and tells would-be suitors that she devotes all her spare time to her children, that they need her. And what man can argue with that?"

"Does she still live up in Yorkshire?"

"No, she moved three years ago." The conversation, Jessica realized, was taking a dangerous direction; it was time to guide it elsewhere. And as she decided exactly where she would steer it, she felt her heart start to hammer erratically against her ribs.

"When we were talking about Amanda the other day..." casually she gathered up another handful of sand "...you mentioned she had a little girl. I remember what lovely blond hair Garth had—does Megan take after him?"

Mitch's lips twisted in a slightly mocking smile. "It would have been something of a minor miracle," he drawled, "if Megan looked like Garth."

Jessica couldn't have been more surprised if he'd come right out and told her about his affair with Amanda. Yet even as she let what he had said sink in, she found herself despising him for the casual way he was discussing the situation.

"Just what are you implying?" she asked, purposely lacing her tone with disbelief. "That Garth was not Megan's father?"

CHAPTER EIGHT

MITCH lay back on his towel, his hands clasped behind his head, his eyes closed. Jessica could have sworn she saw a smile flicker over his perfect lips. And his arrogance, his sheer cockiness, made her feel like slapping him.

"Is that what I was implying?" he asked, his tone lazy.

"I don't know." He was playing with her, and obviously relishing his feeling of superiority... but what he didn't know, couldn't know, was that she knew far more about the situation than he could possibly imagine. He was unaware that she knew of the sordid triangle his involvement with Amanda had formed at Stokely Manor. "You tell me. *Was* Garth the child's father?"

She was looking down at him as she spoke, and now she saw him open one eye and cock an indolent glance up at her. "No," he said softly, so softly she might not have been able to be sure what he said had she not seen his lips form the negative answer. "Garth was not Megan's natural father."

Incredulous, Jessica swallowed hard in the face of Mitch's brazen audacity. The man was utterly vile! She wanted nothing more than to get away from him, never see him again, yet some force within her was determined to see this thing out to the bitter end, to coerce him into admitting the truth... a truth that she had always, in a small and Pollyannalike corner of her mind, hoped would in the end turn out to be a lie. "I don't suppose," she said in a tone of grim cynicism, "that you're about to tell me who was."

"No," he said. "I can't do that."

Jessica closed her eyes and turned from him, hiding her expression of pain. She started as she felt his hand grip her wrist, and as he pulled her toward him, the movement unexpected, she was caught off balance. To her dismay she toppled against him, falling over his chest, with her face just inches from his. But before she could jerk herself upright again, he looped one arm around her and hauled her right over him, then cupped her head with one strong hand, capturing her rigidly.

"And the reason I can't—" his breath was flavored with the taste of the red wine "—is not that it's a private affair, because it isn't. It's common knowledge..."

Her breasts were crushed against him, her legs tangled with his. Flesh to flesh. Skin to skin. Heart to heart. She could feel the strong rhythmic hammering in his chest mingling with the lighter, faster heartbeat in her own. And even as she tried to concentrate on what he was saying, tried to decipher every nuance in his tone, in an effort to separate the lies from the truth, and tried to ignore the blatant intimacy of their physical situation, she found herself becoming overwhelmed by the rich sexuality flowering so relentlessly between them. They might as well have been naked, she realized despairingly, for all the barrier their flimsy clothing provided. Every instinct screamed at her to move, but she knew only too well that the slightest attempt to slide from him would only exacerbate her situation.

Vaguely, she realized he was still speaking, and she wanted to know...needed to know...what he was going to say. Gritting her teeth, she ignored the sweet ache spreading like thick honey through her body, ignored the way he was massaging her skull with his long clever fingers, and forced herself to concentrate on his words.

"...common knowledge," he was repeating, "that Megan is not Garth's child. You see, my sweet, suspicious, always-ready-to-believe-the-worst Jessie, little Megan came into Garth's life as a stranger. She was not his natural child, but neither," he said quietly, "was she Amanda's. Their little girl was adopted."

Jessica stared down at him in disbelief, his words snapping her wantonly scattered thoughts to attention the way nothing else could have done.

How on earth could Amanda have passed off her baby as being adopted? And why? Why had she come up with such a thing? Was it because she'd been afraid her baby would look not like Garth, but Mitch, that she had invented the lie? But how could she have gotten away with it? The very idea was preposterous! Nobody could hide a pregnancy...at least, not in the latter stages. Could they? But perhaps Amanda had managed to do just that. Perhaps she had gone away somewhere, on a "long holiday"...perhaps—Jessica's heartbeats skittered to a suddenly faster tempo and she found it hard to breathe—perhaps even here.

"Why the faraway look, Jessica?" Mitch's voice was silky. "What are you thinking?"

"Oh..." With a huge effort, Jessica gathered herself together. "I was actually thinking of something totally unconnected to what you were just saying. You told me once that...Garth was the one who found Starlight. Had he come here on holiday?"

"Yes, he and Amanda did, on their own."

"Oh, before they adopted Megan, then?"

"Yes, it was. Garth could only stay for a few days, he had to get back to work, but Amanda stayed on. For several weeks, actually."

Jessica felt her head spin. So...she had been right. And the cool way Mitch spoke about the whole thing just proved what a devious and uncaring person he was.

But even as she told herself how she despised him, she realized he had started running his hands up and down her back, his fingertips catching on the tie of her bikini with each teasing stroke. Caught by surprise, she wriggled irritably, forgetting her previous decision not to make even the smallest movement. It was a mistake of the worst kind. His gaze darkened and even as she drew in a sharp, hissing breath, she saw his eyes close, his features twist, as if suddenly he was in great pain, and his body became rigid.

Again, as she had earlier, she sensed a change in him; and she sensed he didn't welcome the desire that was obviously coursing through him. He didn't want it...

But neither did *she* want the honey-sweet sensation flooding her own body. Did he feel the way she did? she wondered dizzily. Wanting...but fighting against that want? Did he feel, too, as if his resistance was being drained away? He did; of that she was sure, as she saw how taut his features were, saw how he had pressed his head back against the towel as if he wanted to escape from her. And as she looked down at him, suddenly something contrary in her, something as alien to her as it was alarming, drove her to try to pierce that invisible armor he had constructed in an attempt to protect himself from his own emotions.

Jessica knew, in a logical corner of her mind, that she should be ashamed of what she was going to do, but she cast logic to the winds as she gave in to a dark and compelling urge to seduce this man who seemed bent on fighting the needs of his flesh.

Jessica dropped her cloudy gaze to his lips. They were slightly parted, and slightly moist. And more than slightly tantalizing. In fact, they were utterly irresistible.

With her hair falling in a sleek curtain around her cheeks, she lowered her head and in a crazily abandoned mood such as she'd never known before, she touched her mouth to his, the kiss sensual yet light as a falling petal. Still, he didn't respond to her kiss—but neither did he pull back. Jessica's blue eyes narrowed, watching for a reaction, her gaze fixed on his eyelids as she moved her lips over his, hesitantly at first but then boldly. He was, she sensed with a thrill of rising excitement, steeling himself, deliberately holding back. And there was a challenge in that that sent Jessica's blood pulsing savagely through her veins.

Unexpectedly, Mitch grasped her shoulders and rolled her over in one swift, powerful movement. In a flash, he had reversed their positions. His eyes—slitted, icy, glittering—looked down at her, piercing her cloudy, desire-blurred gaze.

"This wasn't meant to happen," he said grimly, a muscle trembling in his jaw. "But..."

His words were lost in her mouth as he clamped his lips to hers, his kiss fierce and voluptuous, carrying on where she had left off. "This is what you want," he muttered in a dark, thick voice, "is it, Jessica?"

Her only reply was a tiny guttural sound in her throat.

Eyes never leaving hers, he rested his lower body more heavily on her, and, supporting himself with only that weight, and with his left arm, he slid his right hand deliberately along the warm curve of her shoulder, on an unerring route to the swell of her breast.

Jessica felt as if her throat had closed up. Tight, painful, aching, it resisted as she tried to swallow. Her eyes closed as she could no longer bear to look up into his unfocused gaze, her heartbeats raced headlong to oblivion.

All she was capable of was raising her arms to twine them around his neck, to pull him closer, to close the gap between their mouths once more and seek his kiss as if she would die if he didn't set his flesh again on hers.

The sun beat scorchingly down upon them, on the deserted white beach, the only living creature watching them a white bird gliding along the water's edge.

The beat of its wide wings throbbed in the pulsing air as it flew over them, a hoarse cry coming from its long pointed beak as it reached the topmost branch of the palm tree nearby. But it was a sound that no one in the world heard . . .

Least of all, the two people making love in this perfect paradise.

"We'll have a quick nap in the shade of these palms, and then I'll get you back to Starlight long before your ferry comes in."

That's what Mitch had said, his voice drowsy—and showing no sign whatever of the preoccupation she'd sensed in him before he'd succumbed to her advances—when he'd pulled her close in the afterglow of their lovemaking.

And she had believed him. And why wouldn't she? Besides, the idea of a quick nap had appealed; she'd felt exhausted, although in an intensely pleasurable and contented way. She'd had absolutely no regrets about what they had done. It had been wrong, of course, but it had been inevitable. Mitch may not have intended, initially, to have had sex with her, but she was sure that, before the afternoon was out, it would eventually have happened. The chemistry between them was too strong for it to have been otherwise.

Yet she must have been more tired than she'd realized; either that, or the wine had knocked her for six, for she fell into a deep sleep.

When she finally awoke and looked at her watch, she gave a cry of alarm. It was way after five o'clock!

Scrambling hastily to her feet, with a, "Mitch, it's so late, we have to go!" she looked around . . . and realized, to her consternation, that he wasn't there. His towel was gone, and so was he. And the beach was deserted.

"Mitch?" Her shrill voice echoed back at her from the trees, but the only other sound was the protesting caw of some huge white bird she'd disturbed in the palm tree above, which now took off with a loud flutter of wide wings.

Snatching up her towel, Jessica stumbled away along the path to the cabin, expecting to find him there. Perhaps he'd gone to lock up.

He wasn't there. Not in the main room, not in the bedroom...and not even in the outside toilet. Its ancient door hung desolately open.

"Mitch?" Till now, Jessica had managed to keep her initial feeling of panic under control, but as she stared around the empty cabin, she felt it flare up wildly. Where was he? Surely nothing could have happened to him?

Whirling around, she ran back to the beach, her heart hammering. Dusk, she suddenly noticed, was beginning to fall; the sun was sinking fast below the horizon, its farewell rays glistening pink on the darkening waters. Heartbeats jerking around like puppets on a string, she clutched her trembling hands together and pressed them against her stomach, hunching over to relieve a feeling of nausea as she cast a desperate gaze around her.

And that was when she noticed something she hadn't noticed before...

Noticed it with a feeling of disbelief, stunned disbelief, disbelief that turned quickly to horror, her legs wobbling and threatening to give way under her. Distractedly, she swatted away a cloud of tiny gnatlike things that had started to buzz around her, barely aware of their pinprick bites on her bare arms as she stared aghast at the scene before her.

On the sand where Mitch had pulled the boat that morning were rough, deep grooves where the hull of the small vessel had dragged. The grooves were still there, she could see the shadows, dimly, in the fast-fading light.

But the boat, the sturdy little boat that Ben had loaned Mitch, was no longer beached where he had left it.

It was gone.

In the white light from the moon, Jessica trudged from the cabin to the beach, trailing a heavy bed cover with her.

The sun had been down for some time now, and although she had sat against the trunk of a palm tree on the beach for a long time, the heat of the day had eventually died, and she had become chilled. Although common sense told her to go to bed and try to sleep, she felt drawn to stay on the beach, where she could at least see the water, and watch for the lights of any approaching boat. Not that she had any hopes of being rescued that night...

After she had recovered from the initial shock of discovering that the boat was gone, she had paced back and forth along the water's edge for an hour, trying to figure out what could have happened to it...and to Mitch. She had come up with several possible scenarios—the worst of which was that while she slept strangers had murdered him, stolen the boat, and were only waiting till dark before murdering her, too—and in the end had dismissed all but two possibilities, both of which made sense to her. The first—that for some reason unknown to her, Mitch had deliberately deserted her but would eventually come back, or send someone else to pick her up. The second—that Mitch had gone for a trip on the boat while she slept, and had been unable to return because of some malfunction of the outboard motor. Either way, it was only a matter of time before they were both reported missing and a search party sent out.

Now, cocooned in the heavy cover, she lowered herself against the tree trunk again, tucking herself in carefully. It was quite cosy, really, and thankfully she had never been nervous of bugs nor afraid of the dark. She looked up at the sky, and felt her breath catch at sight of the royal purple backcloth sequinned with diamond stars, felt a sense of awe as she watched trails of wispy cloud drift past a moon whose brightness cast a strange, ghostly glow on the surface of the ocean. With an ache in her heart, she let her eyelashes drift closed and listened to all the night noises blend in a sleepy lullaby: the whisperings of the surf, the murmur of the breeze in the palm fronds above, the rustle in the grass as creatures settled for the night.

She didn't know whether to be furious with Mitch, or worried sick about him. Furious, that he had deserted her; or worried sick because he might be out there somewhere in the boat, unable to get back. If only she could decide how she should be feeling, then perhaps she could settle down, like the little creatures in the grass, and fall asleep.

Fat chance...

"Jessica, wake up!"

Jessica gave a protesting whimper and, curling her body more tightly, shrugged off the hand tugging at her shoulder.

"Jessica, do waken. Look, I've brought you a flask of coffee to warm you up. Good heavens, girl, why didn't you spend the night in the cabin? It would have been so much more comfortable."

Groggily, Jessica opened her eyes, and blinking, put up an arm to shade the brightness. "Put the light out," she muttered, her voice still rough with sleep. "It's too—"

"Jessica—" Firm hands hauled her upright, and as she finally came awake, and focused her eyes, she saw, to her astonishment and bewilderment, that the hands belonged to Ben. "Are you all right? Talk to me, for heaven's sake!"

"Ben?" Again, Jessica found herself blinking like an owl brought from dark to light. "What on earth...?"

But as she looked around, and saw the beach, the smooth turquoise waters...and the grooves on the sand, alongside a very familiar-looking boat...everything came back to her. Her heart seemed to leap into her throat. "Mitch," she said in a choked voice. "Where is he? Is he all right?"

Ben, usually so cheerful, looked uncharacteristically somber. "Mitch is fine," he said. "I'm sure he'll explain everything to you, next time he sees you, but—"

"Where is he?" Jessica felt chilled. Last night she had hauled her shorts and shirt on over her bikini, before dragging the heavy blanket off the bed, but now, even though she was standing there with the blanket wrapped around her, clutching it tightly against her chest, despite the warmth from the early morning sun, she still felt chilled.

"He's gone—" Ben frowned, his irritation plain. "Left Starlight by helicopter an hour ago."

"I don't understand!" Jessica shook her head, her eyes blank. "Where did he go last night? Why did he leave me here alone?"

"You weren't alone." Ben sighed heavily. "Mitch beached the boat on the other side of the promontory—"

"But where was he, all night?"

"Close by, apparently. Look—" He put up a hand as Jessica would have burst in with further questions. "I'm sorry, Jessica, that's all I know. He's going to be in touch with you, sometime in the next few days, he said—concerning some affair the two of you have to settle? I can't remember exactly how he worded it. But till then, I'm afraid, you'll just have to hold your patience. The whole thing's a mystery to me. I knew nothing of what was happening other than that Mitch asked me yesterday if he could take you here for the day, and that he planned you'd both stay overnight—''

''He *planned* that? I can't believe it! He promised he'd get me back to Starlight for the evening ferry! Ben, I have to get to Pointe-à-Pitre within the hour to catch my plane to Antigua, otherwise I'm going to miss my connecting flight—''

''No problem, Jessica. Mitch has arranged for a helicopter to take you directly to Antigua—it's on standby right now on the landing pad behind the inn.'' As Jessica's mouth fell open, he grimaced apologetically. ''High-handed of him, I know... but then, that's Mitch for you. And he'll explain everything, I'm sure, when he sees you—''

''So he took the boat back to the hotel this morning,'' Jessica finally managed, ''asked you to pick me up— left you to do all his dirty work?''

''That's about the size of it. Look, lass, I brought a flask of coffee for you.'' Ben rummaged in a canvas bag lying close by the tree. ''I'll pour you a mug and you can drink it while I check out the cabin. We can talk on the way back, if you like, but there's not much point— I don't know much more than you do yourself. But I tell you this, Mitch's mother is not too pleased with him, the way he's behaved. She's beside herself this morning. I—''

''Mitch's *mother*?'' Jessica stared confusedly at Ben, who was busy pouring steaming coffee into a ceramic mug. ''Mitch's *mother* is annoyed with him? But—''

''Mmm.'' Ben handed her the mug. ''Oh, normally he can do no wrong, as far as she's concerned, but even

Alison draws the line at leaving a woman alone here all night—at least, letting that woman *believe* she's alone. There you are—and you take it black, I remember that from our lunch the other day. Now, hang on a minute, and I'll be right back.''

With that, he tramped away along the path to the cabin... leaving Jessica staring after him, her eyes wide and stark with disbelief. Alison was Mitch's mother? Oh, dear God...

But astounded though she was, Jessica felt all the facts fall into place one after the other, click, click, click. Mitch had been put up for adoption as a baby, she knew that; and all the things he had told her about Alison— she had been the one who opted out of the relationship; a relationship which went ''a long way back,'' was how Mitch had described it; and Alison was the one who had started it up again. Had she known the identity of the couple who had adopted Mitch? If so, she would have had no difficulty keeping tabs on them, and on Mitch, all those years when they had been separated.

It was a story, she realized, that had had a happy ending. Mitch and his mother had been reunited, and obviously had a good relationship.

Jessica sighed. How she had misjudged him... and Alison, too. And she would never have known, had Ben not said what he had just said. Obviously he had somehow got the notion that Mitch had told her the whole story. She would have to be careful not to say anything to alert him to the truth.

Gathering herself together as she heard Ben come back along the path, she sipped from the hot coffee, gaining some comfort from it.

''Best take that old blanket with you,'' Ben said. ''Keep you warm on the water. It's early yet, and there's a keen breeze out there.''

"Thanks," she murmured. "I will." Though as she spoke, her mind was not on the blanket, but on something that had just occurred to her, something that jolted her heart. She'd been so ready to judge both Mitch and Alison on the strength of a few casually overheard words; was it possible that she had been wrong, too, about Mitch and Amanda?

But as her mind veered back to that day at Stokely Manor, and their low, tense voices echoed once more in her head, she knew she hadn't been wrong. That situation had been a different one altogether. She had *heard* Amanda say her child was Mitch's, had *heard* Mitch admit the child was his. What more damning evidence did she need?

The man was contemptible, and she hoped never to set eyes on him again. Yet...he was, apparently, planning to look her up, to press her to make a decision regarding his offer of a "permanent affair." Surely he would never find her? Unless, of course, he connected his failure to acquire the Markington Estate with her visit to Starlight. But why should he? She hadn't by so much as a hint given away anything of her job, her whereabouts, or her new life. And he hadn't found her when she had run out on him before.

But then, he hadn't really been looking for her before. That much she had gathered. Now, things were different. He still wanted her, and believed she might be "available."

Ben pushed the boat into the gently lapping water, and Jessica clambered in, shuddering as she slipped her sandals onto her wet feet and wrapped the blanket more tightly around herself as she sat down. But even in the shelter of the blanket's warmth, she felt as cold as a marble statue, unable to shake off a premonition of impending doom.

CHAPTER NINE

"MITCH CARRADINE," Antonia exploded, "is a rat!"

"I know." Jessica had just spent the past half hour telling her sister everything that had happened on Starlight, and Tonia's response was exactly what she'd expected; now as her sister leaned back in her chair, her lovely oval face suffused with anger, Jessica got up from the kitchen table and crossed to the window. Jason was playing out in the patch of back garden, in his sandbox, well wrapped up in a red quilted jacket, jeans, and a knitted blue hat. She had sent him out there while she talked to Antonia, unwilling to chance his overhearing anything she said. Now she sighed as she turned around again and, leaning her hips against the countertop, said, "I can hardly believe that this time yesterday I was on an island in the Caribbean, under a blazing hot sun."

"Winter's still here, love," Antonia said. "After all, it's only mid-January. Now," she added as she got up and brought her coffee mug to the sink, "I want you to think over what Fen said when you called her—she's right, you know. You ought to give in your notice at work and get out of here. Fen has been after you for a while to pay her a visit, but now that Morag has left her in the lurch in the bookshop, the timing is ideal. Fen can give you a job, and a place to stay till you find somewhere on your own ... if that's what you want. You need to get away from here, Jess—this business has turned you into a nervous wreck! Your eyes are like great dark pools in the back of your head. Good Lord, next thing your face is going to start twitching, and then where will you be?'' She glanced at her watch and went on frustratedly. ''I wish I could stay but I have to pick the twins up from their swimming lesson. Now, talk with your landlady, give in your notice at work, *and start packing your things*! It won't take you long,'' she added with a bleak twist of her lips, ''you don't *have* much.''

After Antonia left, Jessica washed the coffee things, and then wandered aimlessly through the small flat. Normally she would have been at work by now, with Jason safely at the day care down the street; but she had phoned in sick. She just couldn't face Eric Trenton, couldn't face seeing him look so triumphant, couldn't face seeing the knowing look in his eyes—that look of smug awareness that she was no better than he was, in fact, even more deceitful.

She *should* start packing...but as she heard Jason come in from outside, calling out, ''Mummy, what can I do now?'' and stamping his little boots on the mat to shake off the sand, she decided to put it off till tomorrow. Today would be for Jason. She would take him by bus to his favorite new playground at Berrytown Park, then they would have lunch out before taking in a matinee—the new Disney movie he'd been longing to see. Perhaps it would help her relax.

Jason was tugging off his knitted hat as he came into the kitchen, and as he tossed it onto the table, his thick nut-brown hair spilled down over his forehead, and his eyes, golden and shining with good health, looked up at Jessica.

''I missed you when you were away, Mummy, but I had fun with Dominic and Rebecca. Blue Gate is nice, isn't it? Why do we have to live here, Mummy?''

They had talked about this before, many times, but Jason couldn't seem to understand she had to live close to where she worked, and couldn't afford anything better in this area. He was a fastidious child, and hated the dirty street out front, hated the traffic that belched foul fumes as it passed their front door, hated the soot that clung to his toys in the tiny pocket of garden where he played.

She forced her expression into a cheery smile. "How would you like to go to Scotland for a while?" she asked. Scooping him up and setting him on the edge of the table, she put her arms around him and went on. "Your Aunt Fen has invited us to stay with her, for as long as we want."

"I remember Aunt Fen." Jason nodded self-importantly. "She came to see us last summer. She brought me a picture book. She's Aunt Tonia's twin. I liked her. OK. When will we go?"

Jessica smiled, a real smile this time. He made it all sound so simple, didn't he? But after all, it was simple. She could talk to her landlady this evening, and tomorrow she'd tell the office manager at Trenton's that she was leaving. She wouldn't be working out the obligatory two weeks' notice, and so would forfeit the holiday pay she had coming to her, but Fen had a job for her at the bookshop.

"Then that's settled," she said firmly. "Now, we're going to go out for the day, so take your jacket off and let's get you into the bathroom for a tidy-up. Tonight we'll phone Aunt Fen, and tomorrow we'll start packing."

"Aunt Fen lives on her own, doesn't she, Mummy?" Jason asked as she washed his face. "Why doesn't she have any children, like Aunt Tonia?"

"Why don't you ask her that yourself?" Jessica said. "You're going to be seeing her soon!"

Very soon. The knowledge gave her a warm feeling. And when she moved, she would cover her tracks. She would leave no forwarding address with her landlady, and no forwarding address at the office.

That way, if and when Mitch came looking for her, he would come to a dead end.

Jessica slept better that night than she had for some time, but she woke early, while it was still dark. Snuggling under the covers, she decided to steal another ten minutes in bed before getting up to make herself a cup of tea. There was a lot to be done today, all the packing—

The doorbell rang, its insistent peal bringing her to a wide-awake state in an instant. She switched on her bedside light as she swung her legs over the edge of the bed, and saw that it was barely seven. Who on earth could be calling at this time? Oh, surely there couldn't be something wrong with any of the family—Antonia or the twins, or Fen up in Scotland—

Her bedroom faced the street, and she peered out into the dark. She didn't have a clear view of whoever was at the door, could just make out a bulky dark shape— a man's shape. And at the other side of the poorly lit street, she could see a car, highly polished, some black powerful thing that she didn't recognize . . . but then, she had no interest in cars, and even in daylight, would probably not have known the make.

With both hands, she raked her long hair back from her face before flinging on her robe and fastening it tightly around her waist. Her heart was beating giddily. Whoever it was could only be bringing bad news; good news could always wait till daylight.

She felt her stomach churning unpleasantly as she hurried to the front door. Jason's little cubbyhole was at the back of the flat, away from the noise of the street, though she knew that once asleep, nothing short of an earthquake would waken him before eight.

The bell pealed again, just as she switched on the light in the living room and the one in the hallway. She crossed, quickly, to the door, and froze there, fingers of her right hand clutched around the brass knob.

"Who is it?" she called, her voice low.

"Eric Trenton! Open this damned door before I kick it down!"

Jessica's eyes widened in dismay. Eric Trenton? What could he want? He sounded, she realized, furious. But why? Heartbeats thumping more erratically than ever, Jessica pulled back the chain and then unlocked the door, before stepping back into the hall.

Her employer stormed into the flat, slamming the door behind him with a bang that reverberated painfully in her ears. With him, he brought into the small area the dank, sooty smell that always permeated the sunless street, and Jessica shrank... both from it, and from the man himself. His face was mottled with anger, his eyes almost bulging out of their sockets.

"You bitch!" He grabbed Jessica by the shoulders and shook her so hard her teeth chattered. "You lying little bitch. If I'd had you in the room when the fax came in this morning from Lester Forgan's lawyer, I'd have wrung your neck. Did you think you could get away with it? Playing both sides down the middle? How much did Carradine pay you, to send me the wrong information? My God, if—"

"The wrong information?" The words came chokingly from Jessica's throat. "No, it wasn't the wrong information!" Using all her strength, she wrenched herself free from his grip, and, stumbling back from him, crossed her arms around her waist in a defensive gesture. She felt as if every drop of blood had drained from her face. "And what I gave you, I didn't get from him. I saw it myself, saw the reply to the message he sent with his bid. It came from his office on the Saturday, from his right-hand man, confirming the amount, and naming the Markington Estate—"

"He canceled that offer and put in a second bid just minutes before the cut-off time!" Trenton spat the words at her. "Either he fooled you, or the whole thing was a setup—"

"No," Jessica protested. "It couldn't have been a setup. Mitch had no idea why I was there—"

"Look, I don't know what you're up to, but whatever it is, I'm warning you you're playing a dangerous game, and you're going to pay—"

"You're..." Jessica felt as if her throat was closing up. "You're not going to tell Mitch about—"

"About his son?" Eric Trenton's face twisted in an ugly mocking sneer. "Now there's the only amusing part of this whole scenario. No, I'm not going to tell Mitch Carradine he has a son—"

Jessica's breath came out in a trembling moan.

"Nor did I ever have any intention of telling him he has a son. Ah, that shocks you, doesn't it? I can just read your little mind now, as it whirls around trying to make sense of what I'm saying. Well, let me explain."

He came so close to Jessica that she could smell his breath, oily and garlic-tainted, but she stood her ground, forcing herself not to cringe from him, although everything in her shrank back in disgust.

"Mitch Carradine," he said, his voice cold with contempt, "would like nothing more than to know he has fathered a child. A son. He has everything else in this world that he wants, except a child to carry on his name. And why should he have that child?" Trenton's face came closer still, so that Jessica could almost feel the hard stubble on his jaw abrade her own soft cheeks. "When he was the reason my own child died!"

Jessica blinked, and for a long moment there was no sound in the hall but his harsh, unsteady breathing, and the rumble of early morning traffic as it passed by on the cobbled road outside. "What are you talking about?"

''He never told you?'' Trenton's laugh was bitter. ''No, he wouldn't. It doesn't show him up in a very good light. You've met my wife, Nerine?'' he asked abruptly.

''Not . . . really . . . met her. I . . . saw her once, at one of our office parties—''

''Ten years ago, she was Mitch Carradine's mistress—'' Eric Trenton broke off, and rubbed a hand over his eyes. The gesture had so much weariness in it that Jessica—despite the dismay and horror racing through her—felt a sudden, albeit reluctant, surge of sympathy for him.

''I don't know about you,'' she said tersely, ''but I need a cup of coffee.'' Without waiting for a response, she turned and went into the small kitchen, and with a few economical movements, put on the automatic filter coffee maker. Mitch . . . and Nerine Trenton. She shuddered. Vaguely, as the coffee began to drip into the pot, she heard her employer pace back and forth in the hall, overheard him mutter to himself, burst out with bitter exclamations, the odd succinct oath . . .

She poured two mugs of coffee, and turned around with one in each hand. ''Here,'' she said, and he came in from the hall and took the mug without a word.

''Do you take anything in—?''

''No,'' he snapped.

Jessica didn't, either, usually, but now she poured in two heaped spoonfuls of sugar, and stirred in some cream, before sipping from the mug. Never, she thought bleakly, had she needed a cup of hot coffee more.

''So.'' She looked at him with a taut expression. ''You were saying . . . about . . . Mitch and your wife?''

His features were set in a mask that was lined and cruel. ''I knew her long before they met,'' he said in scathing tones. ''We'd been going out for years, we were planning to get married because she was pregnant with my child . . . and then—'' his face contorted ''—she met

Mitch Carradine. Fell for him like a ton of bricks. And knew she'd have no chance with him if he knew she was pregnant.''

He looked away from Jessica, his eyes dull. ''She aborted the baby. Carradine had no idea what the real Nerine was like—selfish, greedy, money-hungry. I knew...but I didn't care. We were two of a kind. I was up and coming...but she thought Mitch would be able to give her more. He was completely taken in by her. I bumped into her one day, and she was on cloud seven. Mitch, she gloated, was going to propose. She was sure of it. I had never expected she would get that far with him, I'd been waiting for him to find out what she was like, and I'd be there to pick up the pieces. But he was more gullible than I'd thought. So...'' He shrugged his bulky shoulders, and his eyes met Jessica's again, and now they were no longer bleak and unfocused, but narrowed and vicious. ''I did what had to be done. I went to see Carradine and I told him the whole story—''

Jessica's soft gasp stopped him, but only for a second.

''He dropped her, of course...and, as I expected, she came running back to me.'' There was more than a trace of self-contempt in his tone when he added, ''And I welcomed her. A month later, we were married. Only then did she tell me something had gone wrong during her abortion, and she wouldn't be able to give me any children.''

A shiver traced its way down Jessica's spine. ''You blame Mitch, and you've never forgiven him,'' she said shakily. ''And you've been trying to get even, ever since.''

''Do you blame me?'' he asked in a harsh tone. ''Would you ever have forgiven me, if I'd done what I threatened and he'd taken your son from you?''

Jessica didn't like Eric Trenton, in fact just looking at him made her skin crawl...yet, as she listened to him, as she saw the pain in his eyes, she wouldn't have been human if she hadn't felt a surge of pity for him.

"Look," she said wearily, "there's nothing anyone can do now, to change what's happened. If, as you say, Mitch's bid was the winning one, then the Markington Estate is now his. Obviously, you're going to have to live with that—"

As soon as she'd said the words Markington Estate, Jessica knew she had made a mistake. Once again, Eric Trenton's face suffused with anger and she saw the veins at his temple bulge frighteningly.

"*Mitch.*" His lips twisted in a sneer. "My God, I can tell by the way you say his name that you're still in love with the man—"

Jessica felt her own anger surge to the surface, but even as she opened her mouth to snap back at her employer, to deny, vehemently, what he had just said, her doorbell rang. Again. She froze, her lips parted, feeling her heartbeats set off on another panicky race. "Who can that be?" The question was addressed more to herself than to the man across the kitchen from her.

"You won't know till you answer the door, will you?" he sneered, his tone rough with impatience.

Jessica moved to the window, and peeped through a chink in the curtains, but it had started to rain, heavily, the wind driving it into a heavy dark sheet, so that visibility was nil.

Who *could* it be? The question raked through her mind as she tightened the belt of her robe and left the kitchen. Head spinning, as she crossed the small hall she called tensely, for the second time in minutes, "Who is it?" But she hadn't locked the door after Eric Trenton's arrival, and even as she walked toward it, she saw the handle turn, and watched, with horrified fascination, as the door swung inward, pushed open by someone outside...

And when she saw the tall figure standing on her stoop, his back to the driving rain, the shock that shuddered through her deprived her, momentarily, of breath.

"Jessica." Her visitor's voice was mild and seemed tinged with amusement. "Aren't you going to ask me in?"

"Mitch!" Throat suddenly so tight she felt as if someone was strangling her, she stumbled back, one hand automatically going to her hair to smooth the sleep-tumbled strands. He was wearing black trousers, a black leather jacket, and with his brown hair darkened by the rain, he had looked, for a moment, like the devil himself. But even the devil, Jessica thought despairingly, could not possibly be possessed of such a lethally charming smile. "What on earth," she choked out, "are *you* doing here?"

"I thought," he said mockingly, following her and stopping when he was just inches from her, looming over her, "that you'd be interested in learning how the Markington Estate affair turned out."

"The Markington Estate?" The words came like a distorted echo from between Jessica's lips.

"Mmm." Mitch's mouth curved in a smug, taunting smile. "It's mine, Jessie, love. As of today, the Markington Estate is mine."

Jessica said nothing, just stared up at him, praying there would be no giveaway expression in her eyes.

Mitch's dark eyebrows rose. "I have to hand it to you, Jess—you really are a cool one. I've just delivered what must be a devastating piece of news—you failed in your mission and now you're going to have to answer to Trenton—but you look as if butter wouldn't melt in your mouth!"

He knew. Or at least, he had guessed—not everything, never everything, thank God—but enough. What

had first aroused his suspicions, she couldn't even begin
to imagine.

But even as she stared at him, her mind whirling
around with unanswerable questions, he grasped one of
her hands firmly and pulled her with him toward the
brightly lit kitchen. Dear God, Jessica thought, feeling
a surge of nausea, when he sees Eric Trenton he's going
to have all his assumptions verified. What he'd only
guessed at before, would be confirmed, beyond a doubt.
He would know just how heavily she'd been involved in
the other man's devious machinations...and he would
deduce, correctly, that Eric Trenton had come here immediately on getting the fax with the news that he'd lost
the bid.

Taking in a deep breath, Jessica steeled herself for the
confrontation that was imminent...and inevitable.

But to her astonishment, the kitchen was empty.

Glancing around blankly, she saw no sign that her
employer had ever been in the flat. The coffee pot was
still in place, the aroma quite strong in the small room,
and her own mug was on the countertop where she had
left it. But the other mug, Eric Trenton's, was nowhere
to be seen. He must, she realized, have slipped out of
the kitchen while she was letting Mitch in, and had—
for whatever reason, decided to make himself scarce till
Mitch left.

And she would make sure he did leave, as soon as she
possibly could. Although Jason was a heavy sleeper, there
was always the possibility that all the comings and goings
would disturb him and he would get up and wander
through to the kitchen, in search of her.

Jessica snatched her hand free and, stepping back from
Mitch, rammed her hands into the patch pockets of her
robe. "What do you want, Mitch? Why have you
come here?"

His smile twisted his face, but there was not one glimmer of warmth in his eyes. "I came," he murmured, "to return something. Something you left behind on Starlight."

Jessica shook her head confusedly. "I didn't," she said, "leave anything be—"

He had slipped one hand into the pocket of his leather jacket and withdrawn something as she was speaking; now, as he held out that something to her, she gave a gasp of dismay... but didn't reach out to take it.

"This, I believe, is yours." His voice was as smooth and hard as polished steel. "You left it in my chalet. It had rolled under the table." The skin around his mouth had tightened, had become white. "Under the computer table," he added, letting his words dangle in the air between them, not needing to say more as he saw Jessica's face turn ashen.

Her pen. The pen with the Trenton Company logo on it. Oh, damn Eric Trenton and damn his conceit! she thought with a feeling of wild hysteria. Why did every single thing connected with him have to have his name on it? But even as the accusing thoughts whirled around in her head, she knew that it wasn't his fault that her part in his plot had been discovered; her own carelessness had been to blame.

"The maid found it, Jessie, the morning we went over to the little island. I had gone back to the chalet, to get my swim things, and she had just picked it up a moment before I came into the room. I can tell you," he said with ominous quietness, "that at first I was unwilling to believe that you had any connection with Trenton... but there was too much at stake for me to trust my instincts. So while you were getting changed for our outing, I went across to the reception desk and asked the girl at the switchboard if you had made any long-distance calls within the last twenty-four hours. Claire had a record of your calls, and it took only minutes for her to find out that the last number you'd asked to be connected to was, indeed, Trenton's office number—''

Jessica made a small sound in her throat, an almost inaudible moan.

''And one well-placed call on my part to a contact in the UK verified what I had then begun to suspect, that you actually work at the Trenton Company.'' Mitch's eyebrows rose again. ''No denial, Jess? No defense?''

Jessica felt as if she were sinking down into some bottomless pit, but she didn't speak, couldn't speak, because she knew that if she did, there was a very good chance she might break down.

''So. . .'' Mitch's eyes were devoid of emotion. ''You and Trenton. . . you're involved. . . romantically?''

At this, Jessica at last found her voice. ''No,'' she burst out hoarsely, protestingly, ''of course we're not. I work for him, that's all—''

Mitch smiled, though again his smile didn't reach his eyes. ''Good. Because even though I now know exactly how untrustworthy you are, my offer still holds—''

''Your offer?'' Jessica breathed the words incredulously.

''You know, Jess—the affair we discussed? A. . . permanent, temporary arrangement? Our Friday affair? Of course, had you been involved—sexually— with Trenton, I should have withdrawn that offer. He is the one man in this world with whom I wouldn't be willing to share you.''

Jessica stared at Mitch disbelievingly. And then, a rage such as she'd never known came burning up inside her like a choking fire. But even as she opened her mouth to tell him exactly what she thought of him *and* his insulting offer, she heard a scuffling noise in the lobby behind her. Oh, dear God, she thought as she whirled around, her hand going to her heart, not Jason. Please, don't let him have wakened—

"For God's sake, what's going on? What's all the noise about, Jess? What does a man have to do to get a good night's sleep in this place? Come back to bed, kitten, and let's get some shut-eye!"

Jessica stared, her mind totally blank, as she took in the scene before her. Eric Trenton—his pale, paunchy, hairless body naked but for a pair of magenta jockey pants—was standing in the doorway, blinking, yawning, scratching his head groggily as if he'd just wakened. Jessica felt her blood turn to ice as her mind grasped what was happening, and reeled in horror from the realization that her initial reading of the situation—that she had stumbled into the middle of some incomprehensible nightmare—was wrong. Oh, so very wrong.

Eric Trenton had deliberately set out to create the impression that they had spent the night together.

Jessica reached out a trembling hand to the edge of the countertop to steady herself. "Why?" The question came out in a choking whisper. "Why would you—?"

"Trenton." Mitch's voice was the voice of a stranger's. "Congratulations. You may not have heard yet that the Markington Estate is now mine, but you appear to be in possession of an even more valuable prize." He turned to Jessica, and Jessica shrank from the stark, devastated look in his eyes.

"I tracked you down and came to you this morning," he said in a voice so taut it was almost unrecognizable, "because I did believe—did even hope—you would have some explanation for what you did, an explanation for your deception. Now I know the reason, and I wish to God I had never come—wish to God I could have kept at least some of my illusions." He reached out and, as if he couldn't help himself, touched her hair, a silky strand that had fallen to coil itself atop her robe, over the lush swell of her breast. "What a tragedy," he murmured thickly, "that such beauty of body could hide such ugliness of spirit."

She hadn't taken the pen from him; now, slowly, he tucked it into the breast pocket of her robe and then, so unexpectedly that she didn't have time to shrink back, he gripped her shoulders, his long powerful fingers so hard she knew the imprint would be with her for hours...perhaps forever.

His smile was cold and bleak as the winter morning, his mouth twisted bitterly. "What do you say we have one for the road, Jessie? One for the scrapbook... memory's scrapbook...wasn't that how you phrased it, on the island?"

Oh, she remembered only too well, saying that to him, remembered the pain she had felt then. But it was nothing to the pain slicing through her now. With a small moan, she tried to slip from his grip, but he only tightened it, and pulled her against him roughly, turning her moan into a gasp as her untrammeled breasts were squashed against his muscled chest. In a swift possessive movement, he slipped one hand to the small of her back, drawing her into him so intimately she could feel the ridged muscles of his lower body digging into her soft flesh. At the same time, he cupped the back of her skull with his other hand, forcing her face up to him so that her neck was painfully arched.

"Here's something for your scrapbook." His eyes had a look of dull, hopeless despair, and at that moment Jessica knew, beyond a shadow of a doubt, that he had forgotten they were not alone. Forgotten...or didn't care.

His kiss was sensual and passionate, open-mouthed and intimate...a kiss sweeter and more poignant than any they had shared before. A kiss from the heart. The contact could have lasted at most only fifteen seconds, but by the time he freed her, Jessica felt as if she were dying, dying from a pain that was beyond any in her lifetime's experience.

"Remember that." He drew the pad of his thumb across her lower eyelid, smearing the tear trembling there, his face drawn and bleached of any vestige of color as she looked up at him through a blurred gaze. "Remember that, sweet Jessie Gray, when you're abed with someone else. *Remember how it was between us*."

He slid the pen from her pocket again, and as he left, he tossed it onto the kitchen table, where it rolled, and rolled, slowly, painfully slowly, endlessly slowly, till it reached the edge, and fell with a tinny clatter to the floor, just as Mitch closed the front door carefully, quietly...and with grim finality...behind him.

And all that time, Eric Trenton hadn't spoken another word. Only the damning words he'd spoken when he'd come to the doorway. But now he looked with an expression of scornful triumph at Jessica as she stood, shuddering, in the middle of the kitchen floor, tears rolling down her cheeks, dripping unheeded on the lapels of her robe.

"I'd say," he announced in a hard voice, "that you and I are quits. You may want Mitch Carradine, but he'll never look at you again. In his eyes, you're trash."

Jessica didn't answer...didn't even move, not till long long after Eric Trenton had left and she had heard the squeal of brakes as he turned at the end of the street.

Only then, her steps the steps of an old and very tired woman, did she leave the kitchen and walk through to her room. Eric Trenton had been in here. His coffee mug sat, half full, on her bedside table. He must have sat on the bed as he took off his shoes and socks. She could see the indentation of the foot of the duvet.

Dully, she crossed to the window, and pulling the curtains aside, looked out. The rain had stopped. The black car was gone.

Mitch's car, the one he must have come in, was gone, too.

And she knew that he would never come to her again. Never speak to her again.

She should have felt relieved, relieved that now she need have no worry that he might find out about Jason and take him away, but all she felt was a misery that was deep and agonizing and unassuageable. The misery of knowing that she was in love, still in love, with Mitch.

And would be, forevermore.

CHAPTER TEN

FENELLA'S bookshop, the Readers' Nook, was situated in the small Perthshire town of Glengower. The granite building had two storys, Fenella living in a flat above the shop with her cat, Sailor, for company. Directly across the street was the Rubber Ducky Play School, where Jessica had enrolled Jason a couple of days before starting her new job.

"Jason has settled in well," Fenella remarked one morning after Jessica had been in Glengower almost a month. The two were between customers, and enjoying a mug of coffee behind the shop counter. "But..." Fenella's normally sweet expression became worried as she scrutinized Jessica's pale face. "I'm afraid I can't say the same about you."

Jessica forced a smile. "I'm fine, honestly. It's just that...since my trip to Starlight...I've found myself thinking a lot about how Jason's going to feel when he's old enough to realize that he has a father somewhere, and that I've deprived them both of their right to know each other."

"I don't think Mitch has any rights where his son is concerned," Fenella said grimly. "And when Jason is old enough, you can tell him exactly why you kept him from his father."

"I plan to keep them apart, if I can...but I won't turn Jason against Mitch," Jessica said in a quiet voice.

Fenella sighed. "No, best not to. I always admired Mum for not trying to sour us on men while she was bringing us up, though with what our father put her through, she had reason enough. But in my case," she went on flatly, "she didn't have to. Tonia and I were only ten when he walked out, but I was glad to see him go. He was an obnoxious b—" She broke off when she saw Jessica's quickly raised eyebrows, and with a shrug, she corrected herself. "*Bully*, then, and a womanizer, without one redeeming feature."

"He's the reason you've never married, isn't he." Jessica's words were in the form of a statement, not a question, and she uttered them in a low, compassionate tone.

"You finally figured that out, did you?" Fenella said wryly.

"Oh, I figured it out a long time ago."

"Funny thing is..." Fenella perched herself on a stool beside the till "...I liked Mitch. I met him only once, but I must admit he charmed me. And he seemed so right for you. I thought there was something very straight about him—only shows how we can never rely entirely on our instincts." She grimaced. "You were only five when our father left, but I know his leaving hurt you just as badly as it did the rest of us... and yet you gave yourself so trustingly to Mitch, so sweetly, as if you'd never been let down by a man before."

"It'll never happen again," Jessica said bitterly. "I've learned my lesson this time. And now I can really understand how Mum felt when Dad left—"

"She was well rid of him!"

"We should be thankful we three took after her, rather than after Dad—I don't think we turned out so badly!"

"You're right." Fenella quirked her little finger as she lifted her mug to her mouth and went on with an affected genteel accent, "We are all such *nice* girls!"

Jessica burst out laughing. Seeing her sister with that exaggeratedly snooty expression on her face, hearing her adopt the same snobbish tone she had used to such effect years ago when she had wanted to tease Jessica out of some unhappy little mood, had, for the moment, pushed her present unhappiness to the back of her mind. "Oh, Fen, you may be thirty-three, but sometimes you act like a schoolgirl!"

The ping of the doorbell had Fenella straightening her face, and Jessica hurrying to the back shop till her giggles subsided. Then, after wiping her eyes with a Kleenex, she slipped quietly into the shop again. The customers were two middle-aged women, obviously well-known to Fenella but strangers to Jessica. As Fenella discussed something with them—apparently some new books one of the women wanted to order—Jessica made her way to the shelf at the back where she'd been dusting earlier.

She'd been there only a couple of minutes, when she heard Fenella say, "Tell me, Mrs. Mackie, how's Jeannie doing?"

"Just grand," the woman replied. "She's to be getting home from hospital the day after tomorrow."

"Super! And have she and Danny decided what to call the new baby?"

"Aye, they have that. He's going to be Robert Struan Mackie, after his two grandfathers."

"That's a good strong name, Mrs. Mackie." Fenella's voice was warm. "Now, dear, I've got your order. I'll give you a ring when the books come in. Allow about a month."

The bell pinged again as the two women left, and Jessica heard Fenella go through to the back, heard her calling "Jessica?" up the stairs leading to the flat, and Jessica called out, "I'm in the shop, Fen, dusting."

"Oh." Fenella came back through the doorway. "I thought you'd gone upstairs for something. That was Nell Mackie and her cousin. A nice woman, Nell, but tends to keep me all morning unless I cut her visit short right at the start."

"She's a new granny?"

"Mmm. It's quite a story really." Fenella went behind the counter and busied herself writing out the order for Mrs. Mackie's books. "Her daughter Jeannie," she went on in an absent tone, "got married three years ago to a fellow from Skye, Dan McLeod, who'd had life-saving cancer surgery when he was younger. Knowing Dan would be sterile after his operation and assuming that farther down the road he might want to marry and have children, his doctor had suggested that they preserve some of his sperm—"

"That can be done?"

"Mmm. They freeze it. Apparently hospitals have been banking the sperm of men with cancer for quite a few years now." Fenella looked up, and smiled. "At any rate, Dan went along with his doctor's suggestion, so after he married Jeannie, she went to an in vitro fertilization clinic in Edinburgh and took part in their program."

"And it worked?" Jessica's curiosity was aroused.

"Not the first time around, apparently, but although the doctors could only offer a twenty percent chance of being successful, she and Dan were lucky the second time they tried." Fenella shook her head, as if she still found it hard to believe. "A minor miracle, don't you think?"

"Yes." Jessica smiled in return. "A minor—"

She broke off abruptly, and Fenella raised her eyebrows. "What is it, Jess?" she asked, and then added, "Whatever's wrong? You look as if you've seen a ghost!"

For a long, taut moment, Jessica just stared in front of her, not really seeing her sister, or even making sense of what she was saying. *A minor miracle*. She had wondered for a fleeting moment why the phrase seemed so familiar, then it had come swooping back into her mind: those were the exact words Mitch had said on the beach, when she had asked if Amanda's baby looked like Garth.

"That would be a minor miracle," he had drawled. And she had assumed he'd been referring to the fact that Garth had not been the father.

She had also assumed that Mitch had been the child's natural father.

But she had not carried on from there. She had not allowed her brain to come up with any scenario that might throw a different slant on that truth...that apparent truth.

Dear God...she struggled to keep from losing her train of thought for things were happening in her brain, things over which she had no control. Facts were meshing with facts, the internal computer in her mind coming up with suggestions and possibilities...both startling and outrageous...and conclusions that had her heart staggering and her blood rushing dangerously to her head.

"Fenella." She tried to keep her voice steady. "Suppose you were married, and your husband couldn't, for some medical reason, make you pregnant, yet you both desperately wanted to have a child...what would you do?"

"Well..." Fenella's gaze was thoughtful. "Adopt, I suppose, or at least, try to. I've heard that nowadays, with the Pill, and with so many single mothers opting to keep their babies, it's not as easy as it once was."

"It's almost impossible. So then—" Jessica's voice was no longer quite so steady "—what would you do?"

Fenella rested her elbows on the counter, and, steepling her hands, let her chin sit in the cleft of her fingertips as she gazed at her sister. "I guess the next step would be to go the route Jeannie and Dan did."

"In vitro fertilization."

"Mmm, and then, of course, we'd have to decide whether we wanted an anonymous donor, or someone we knew." Fenella swallowed, and as she drew herself up straight, Jessica saw a dawning comprehension in her

eyes. "If I were in such a situation, and if my husband
had a brother—even an adoptive brother—whom we
both admired tremendously—" Her voice was tight with
controlled emotion. "Then he would be the ideal choice.
Oh, Jessie, surely you're not thinking that—"

"Yes. I am. Garth and Amanda."

When the idea had exploded in Jessica's brain, in the
first few moments it had all seemed clear to her; now as
Fenella stared at her, waiting, confusion splintered her
mind, and she found it difficult to gather the pieces
together and organize them into logical thoughts. But
finally she did, and felt as if her heart—her whole
being—was falling into space. "It all makes sense,
Fennie," she whispered. "Garth had a rare hereditary
heart disease—such a very serious disease he wouldn't
have wanted to pass it on to a baby."

Fenella hugged her arms around herself. "But of
course he would want Amanda to have a family—"

"And she would want a child as close to Garth as
possible, especially when they both knew he...wouldn't
be around...for too many years."

"Do you think that's what happened?"

Jessica had a heady disconnected feeling, as if she was
at a too high altitude and the air had become so thin it
was painful to breathe.

"It would explain so much," Fenella offered on a soft
breath.

"But Megan...Amanda's daughter...why would Mitch
have told me nobody knew who her father was? Why
would he have tried to make me believe she was an
adopted child?"

Fenella crossed to her sister and, lifting Jessica's cold
hands, held them tightly, her warmth spreading through
Jessica's skin into her blood. And when she spoke, it
was with compassion in her voice.

"I think, darling Jess, the only person who can answer that question for you is Mitch."

Jessica felt her heartbeats jam together. For a long time she just stared at her sister, her vision blurred, her thoughts ascramble, as she tried to quell the feeling of panic gripping her.

"If we're right," she said, her voice catching, "Mitch will never forgive me for having kept Jason from him."

"That may well be the case," Fenella said, pulling Jessica close. "And if that happens, you'll have to find some way to live with it. But if you're right about the baby, and Mitch did do this thing for Garth and Amanda, then he's a man in a million, and he'll find it in his heart to understand. Hold that thought, Jessica, when you go looking for him. It'll help carry you through."

It took only one phone call to the Golden Chain head office to find out Mitch's whereabouts. He was, according to his secretary, at the Markington Estate in Wiltshire, supervising the building contractors who had already begun work on the extensive renovations there.

"Take my car," Fenella had offered right away, but Jessica had declined the invitation.

"Thanks, but it's a while since I've driven and I'm a bit rusty. And the way I'm feeling," she'd added wryly, "I don't think I'm fit to be in charge of a wheeled vehicle. I'd be a danger to myself...and anyone else on the road. Besides, you'll have Jason, and it'll be easier to get around if you have your car. Are you sure you're going to manage, coping with the shop alone during the day, and then coping with him when you pick him up at the Rubber Ducky?"

"With my hands tied behind my back!" Fenella retorted confidently. "I'm not just a pretty face, you know! Now—" she bent over the road map of Britain spread

out on the shop counter ''—you'll have to take the train
to Salisbury, then a bus to Davington. Once there, you'll
probably have to take a taxi to the estate—it looks as if
it's a couple of miles farther on. But—'' She looked up
with a hopeful expression. ''After that, if all goes well,
Mitch will be driving you around in his Jag.''

''He drives a Range Rover,'' Jessica said automatically, and then grimaced. ''Well, he used to. Who knows
what he drives now! At any rate, I'm not counting my
chickens—he may throw me out on my neck after he
hears my story. Then I'll hear from him only through
his lawyers.'' Mitch would, of course, want custody of
Jason; but Jessica kept her thoughts determinedly away
from that contingency. Think positively, that's what
Fenella always said, and that was what she must try to
do.

Still, it was hard, and the following evening as she sat
in the back of a taxi splashing its way up the winding
drive leading to Markington Manor, positive was the very
last word she'd have used to describe the way she was
feeling. And the weather didn't do anything to cheer her
up. It was wintry cold and miserable, leaden rain slanting
in a northerly gale, and the visibility almost nil. Thank
heavens, she reflected as the taxi pulled to a halt, that
she had decided against borrowing Fenella's old Austin.

It had taken her much longer to get here than she'd
counted on, because she had just missed a bus to
Davington, and had to wait two hours in a freezing
waiting room for the next. Once she got to the small
town, there was no taxi immediately available, so she'd
had to wait in a draughty café till one was free. And
now—she glanced at her watch in the dim light inside
the cab as the driver turned to collect his fare—it was
pitch dark and close to seven.

''Thanks, luv,'' the driver said as Jessica paid him.
''Now—'' he peered through the murky night ''—are

you sure there'll be somebody here? Place looks deserted. Would you like me to hang around, till somebody comes to the door?''

"Would you mind?" she asked apologetically. "I wouldn't like to be stranded away out here on a night like this. Could you just wait till somebody comes to the door? I'll give a wave if it's all right, then you can go."

"No problem."

He kept the engine running, but as Jessica hurried to the front steps, clutching her shoulder bag and wincing as the rain sleeted against her cheeks, she heard nothing but the sound of the gale howling around the huge dark house.

What if she had come all this way for nothing? Tugging back her hair from her cheeks as the wind whipped it around her face, she located the bell, an enormous brass pull, and gave it a strong jerk. If it pealed inside, she had no way of knowing. Every other sound was obliterated by the storm blattering around her.

She hunched into the upturned collar of her navy trench coat as an extra-strong gust of wind made her gasp. It looked, she thought despairingly, as if no one was at home. Glancing around at the taxi, she thought she saw it begin to move forward. Panicking, she grabbed the bell pull again, but just as she made to tug it, the fanlight above the door lit up, and seconds later, the door swung inward, creaking, and bright light flooded out in a wide yellow cone.

Jessica recognized Mitch's tall, wide-shouldered figure, his arrogant stance, even though she couldn't see his face, just his bold outline, black against the light behind him. Heartbeats hammering, without turning her head, she lifted her arm, and waved to the cabdriver. She heard, faintly, the roar of the engine as he gunned it, and the crunch of gravel. And as he turned, an arc of bright light swept over the front door area, highlighting Mitch's face for a fleeting second, long enough for Jessica to see the stunned shock in his expression, and then the glow was gone, the sound of the car faded, and Jessica knew she was alone—instinctively knew she was alone at the manor—with Mitch.

Without a word he stepped back into the hall, holding the door open, and without a word, she walked past him. She heard the door shut behind her, heard the sound of a lock clicking into place. Now that the outside was closed off, she could hear her own unsteady breathing, could hear the rain drip from the hem of her coat to the parquet floor. Nervously, she raked her wet hair back from her cheeks, and with her heart in her throat, she turned to face him.

His features were set in lines so grimly forbidding that she flinched as if he'd whipped her with a lash.

"What do you want?" His question came out in a snarl of barely contained anger. "I thought I made it clear, last time we met, that I had withdrawn my offer."

Jessica felt her teeth start to chatter. The hall was unheated, the temperature of the air frigid. But beyond where Mitch was standing, through closed French doors, she could see a fireplace, with flames leaping up the hearth's throat. Yellow flames, warm, welcoming...

"That's not why I've come." Her voice had a faint tremor. "I have something to tell you." She shuddered, an involuntary reaction to the cold air, her wet hair, the rain dribbling down her neck inside the collar of her wool sweater. "But I need to get heated up first." She gestured toward the lighted room. "May I take off my coat and go through to the fire?"

Without waiting for his reply, she dropped her shoulder bag onto a nearby chair, and started to shrug off her soaking trench coat. Before it was half off, Mitch was in front of her, taking it from her, politeness obviously overcoming his feelings of contempt. And in that second when they were close, before he stepped back and slung the coat over the banister of the spiral staircase, she smelled whiskey on his breath. He had been drinking? But how much?

"This way," he snapped, and led the way across the hall.

Hesitating for only a moment, Jessica followed, wiping her cold wet hands along the folds of her gathered skirt. He pushed open one side of the French doors, and stood aside to let her pass into the room. As she did, she was once again very close to him, this time so close her shoulder brushed against his chest, the contact, fleeting though it was, bringing a flush to her cheeks. He was wearing a thick-knit taupe sweater and a pair of blue jeans, faded and soft after many washings, and from him emanated a heat that brought his familiar male scent to her nostrils...a scent that had her nerves quivering in response.

"Sit down." He gestured abruptly toward one of the sofas. Crossing to the hearth, he heaved a huge log atop the half-burned ones already in the fire, setting them sparking and hissing like angry snakes.

When he turned back, Jessica was still standing in the same place, and she saw his lips tighten. Turning away, she walked over to where a leather pouf was positioned in front of a wing chair and, hauling it over the carpet, she settled it on the ornately sculptured Chinese rug in front of the fire and sat down. Mitch, she noticed, had moved to a bar tray set on a low, polished side table.

"Have a brandy," he said curtly as he lifted a crystal decanter. "It'll warm you up more quickly than any fire."

About to decline his offer, Jessica changed her mind. The alcohol would not only give her the extra courage she needed to say what she had come to say, it would also fortify her against the fury she expected to explode

from him when he found out she'd not only given birth
to his son but had kept that son from him.

The brandy he poured was a more than generous
measure; perhaps, despite his reluctance to have her in
his house, he did feel a hint of compassion for her in
her obviously distressed state. She took the glass from
him, his fingertips just barely brushing her cold skin,
and cupping her hands around the glass's crystal bowl,
she took a tentative sip. Glancing up from under her
lashes, she saw Mitch was pouring himself a Scotch.

He didn't come back to the hearth, just stayed where
he was, over by the bar. He stood there, rigid like some
stone statue, watching her, wordlessly, as she sipped from
her glass. How was it possible, Jessica wondered with a
tearing pain in her heart, that eyes so tawny-gold in color
could yet look so wintry-raw and cold? Her nervousness
escalated into panic, and she found herself sipping
mindlessly, almost relishing the raw, burning sensation
as the brandy fired her throat. Yet in a few minutes, it
did its work. She began to feel warm, and calm, and
confident...

And when she put the glass down on the marble
hearth, and looked up at Mitch, she felt only a shred of
the fear she had felt earlier. He was a rational man; he
would listen to what she had to say, and then they would
talk, discuss what was the best thing to do.

She realized, with a jolt of shock, that she had already
persuaded herself that Mitch had not been involved with
Amanda, at least not in the way she had for so long
believed. When had that change of heart occurred? On
the way down to Salisbury in the train? On the long,
slow bus ride? In the taxi? Or had it happened just moments ago, when she had seen Mitch again? Had it been
her deepest instincts coming into play at last, giving her
insight into the truth of the matter?

Whatever...she still needed confirmation, needed to have Mitch look her in the eyes and tell her that he and Amanda had never been involved in an affair. Then, and only then, would she tell him about Jason.

Mitch cleared his throat, roughly, and Jessica sensed that his patience was running out.

Pushing herself to her feet, she stood straight, her hands clasped tightly together at her waist.

"I've come to ask you something," she said. "And...I know it's a very...personal...question, but you must tell me the truth. It's...very important."

Mitch had downed the last of his Scotch and replaced the glass on the low bar counter. Now he stuck his hands into his pockets and regarded her through eyes that were shuttered. "I make no promises."

The fire made a singing noise, drowning out the mellow tick-tick of the antique clock on the mantelpiece, just for a moment or two. Jessica drew in a deep breath. This was it. It was all or nothing now.

"I want to ask you about Megan—" she began, only to be interrupted by Mitch's harsh inquiry.

"Megan? What the devil has Megan got to do with you?"

"Nothing to do with me, Mitch," Jessica said evenly, "but...what does she have to do with...you?"

He stared at her, as if she was out of her mind. "When you talk sense, then I'll answer." His eyes glittered with hostility, his hand flung out in a gesture of extreme impatience.

"Who is Megan's father?" There, it was out. Out in the open, to be tidied up, answered...or not.

Mitch rocked back as if she had threatened to throw something at him. "I told you," he said with bewilderment in his tone, "when we were on the island, that *nobody* knows who Megan's father is. My God, do you mean to say you've come here, on a night like this, to waste my time—?''

''Will you *swear* that's the truth?'' Jessica persisted, dizzy now as a result of the brandy. ''On the Bible?''

Mitch took in a deep breath. She saw his chest rise and fall, once, then twice. And then he turned his back on her. He made for the door. He was going to leave, without ever answering her question. Hysteria and despair rose up inside Jessica, and she ran stumbling after him.

''Tell me, damn you!'' She reached him and grabbed the back of his sweater, pulling it hard to stop him. ''I need to know—*I need to know if Megan is your child!*''

He hadn't been making for the door, but for a bureau alongside it. He turned from it now, his expression that of a man who was having a knife twisted into his heart, over and over and over, the utter incredulity in his eyes sending an ominous chill shivering down Jessica's spine. In his hands, she saw vaguely, was a photograph. A silver-framed photograph. After a frozen, endless moment, he held it out to her, slowly, and after another long, taut moment, Jessica took it from him. And all the time, her eyes were locked with his.

''Look at it.'' His voice was thick. ''And you'll find your answer.''

Jessica closed her eyes. It was the moment of truth; she knew that, as surely as she knew Mitch was watching her, his face closed.

''Look at it,'' he ordered again harshly, and she did.

At first, she couldn't make sense of it. Oh, she recognized Amanda, and she recognized Garth, their faces both bright with happiness... but the child in Garth's arms, a little girl... Jessica felt the ground swaying under her. Oh, dear God, she had been wrong, so very wrong.

''This is Megan.'' Moving like an automaton, Mitch took the photo from her shaking fingers and replaced it with careful precision on the bureau. "The little Vietnamese girl Garth and Amanda adopted after her mother's death. The father was Vietnamese, too, but his identity is unknown."

The brandy was doing its potent work. Jessica felt as if she were floating, as if the world as she knew it no longer existed. All her inhibitions were gone, she had no control over what she was thinking...nor over what she was saying.

As if the voice she was hearing was not her own but that of some stranger, she listened to it echo around the room. "But I heard you and Amanda talking, that day you took me to Stokely Manor. I heard her say she was pregnant. *And·I heard you admit that the child was yours.*"

Mitch froze, his back still to her. She sensed the tightening of his body, felt it as surely as if he was holding her. Everything in him froze.

And then, when she could stand the intensity of the tension no longer, he turned, the movement heavy, and looked down at her with such revulsion in his eyes that it scraped like a sharp knife blade against Jessica's heart.

"So," he said in an ugly, rasping voice, "on the basis of that scrap of overheard, private conversation, you decided, in your Godlike wisdom, that Amanda and I were having an affair."

Jessica's head was spinning, she felt as if she was going to faint. Vaguely, she heard Mitch go on,

"...only part of the story...and so just let me set you straight. Yes, Amanda was pregnant—she did, however, lose that baby. She miscarried, at four months. My child? Yes, it was my child, but only in the most basic of ways. You see, because of Garth's hereditary heart problem, doctors had advised·him not to..."

Jessica was still staring at him, but not really seeing him. Not even really hearing him anymore, because she didn't *need* to hear him, didn't need to hear what he was saying. She already knew. Her instincts had already told her. Garth and Amanda had asked for his help...and he had not refused them.

Oh, God, what had she done?

Tears welled up inside her, deep in her soul. What she had done was judge him without being in possession of all the facts. She had believed the worst of Mitch, walked out of his life...and taken his unborn son with her.

He would never forgive her. Fenella had been wrong. It was too much for any man to forgive.

She saw, through blurred eyes, that he had turned away from her, had gone back to the bar, where he stood, palms flat on the low, polished wood surface, his arms rigid, his whole body rigid, his head bowed as if he was weighed down with pain.

This would be as good a time as any, Jessica thought anguishedly, to flee.

Sobs rising uncontrollably in her throat, tears running down her cheeks, her footsteps muffled by the thick carpet and a sudden hissing of the fire, Jessica ran from the room. Throwing on her coat in the front hall and scooping up her bag as she went, she ran to the door, unlocked it, and once outside, in the gale, she ran hysterically down the steps.

The night was dark as pitch. But she knew her way down the drive, and once she got out onto the road, she would set off for Davington. It was only a mile or so away. There she would find an inn for the night. And one thing she needn't fear, she thought, feeling as if her heart had broken into a million bleeding pieces, was that Mitch would come after her.

If he had despised her before, it would be as nothing to what he would feel for her now. She had accused him of being Megan's father, and had let him know she believed he'd had an adulterous affair with Amanda...

The wind howled in the trees—echoing the howling of despair in her soul—as she kept running. Soon, she thought, she must reach the road. But she had somehow lost her bearings and must have veered off the drive in the dark, because now she was running on wet grass, soggy grass, and it seemed to be trying to drag her back, seemed to be telling her she was going in the wrong direction.

Go back, it warned. Go back...

But she kept going, blindly kept going, the brandy wiping out the logical part of her brain, the part that tried to tell her perhaps she was running into danger.

And when the danger came, by that time it was too late. She felt the ground give way suddenly under her feet, and as it did she screamed. The sound rent the air, just for a moment, and then it was drowned out by the fury of the gale.

And as she tumbled forward, headlong into space, reaching out desperately but to no avail for a handhold as she fell over and over, down and down, into a seemingly bottomless pit, her wail of terror was lost in the night.

CHAPTER ELEVEN

JESSICA floated, feeling lazily weightless, totally relaxed. She was in a shadowy but pleasant world, all alone, and sensed she had been for some time. She liked it that way. Liked the peace, the absence of worries of any kind...

But just when she felt herself begin to drift more deeply into the lovely drowsiness, she imagined a child's voice tugging at her, at her heart, like a silken thread attached to her emotions, shaking them. It disturbed her feeling of serenity, and she parted her lips to whisper something, a protest. But though she was sure she had spoken, sure she had said, "Go away," she heard no sound. No sound from her lips. Yet close by, she could have sworn she heard a whisper, and a scuffle. The scuffle of feet on a polished floor? Scurrying, hurrying feet? But even as she tried to concentrate her mind and interpret the noises, she felt a dull pain throbbing in her arm, and she moaned.

And in response to that sound, she heard a definite murmur. Then she felt a cool palm on her forehead, followed moments later by something brush up her arm. She winced as she felt a sting on the flesh there.

A wasp. She tried to say the word but wasn't sure if she was being heard or not. A wasp. I've been stung...

The voice...a woman's voice...hushed her. "It'll help you sleep," it said gently. "Just sleep."

I don't want to sleep, she tried to say. I want to...

But once again, she sank down into the inky black space, and everything was swallowed up in silence.

Next time she surfaced, the pain in her arm was gone.

She was in bed. She didn't open her eyes, it was too much bother, but she could tell she was in bed. She wasn't sure if she had realized that before. And it was a hard bed, much harder than the one she had at home. The blankets were lighter, too, the pillows softer. She inhaled, and became aware of a faint antiseptic smell that transported her back in time, to the days she spent in hospital when Jason was born—

Jason.

She opened her eyes abruptly as reality hit her with a starkness that had her body snapping out of its lethargic state. And the moment her eyes opened, she heard a breathless whisper from close by.

"Jessica!"

She blinked, and found her hand caught up in a firm, warm clasp.

"Oh, Jessie, thank God..."

It was Antonia. Leaning over her. Antonia, with her lovely dark hair uncharacteristically lank, her oval face drawn and pale, and tears in her beautiful green eyes.

"Tonia?" Jessica's voice came out in a croak. "What happened? Where am I?"

"You're at Davington Cottage Hospital. Jessie, I'll be right back—I have to get Dr. Gough—we've been so worried—"

Jessica clutched her sister's hand as she made to move away. "Jason." Desperation made her voice even more hoarse. "Is he all right? Is he still with Fenella?"

She felt her heart clench as she saw a flicker of...something...cross Antonia's features. "Jason's fine, darling, absolutely fine. Now..." She gently tried to draw her hand away. "I'm going to get the doctor—"

Jessica's grip tightened. "What happened to me, Tonia? Why am I here?"

Antonia paused for just a second, and then said evenly, reassuringly, "You had an accident...at Markington Manor...the night you went to talk with Mitch. His workmen had been excavating on the grounds that day, and apparently there was an underground tunnel nearby that nobody knew about—the rainstorm caused the earth to subside into it, and in the dark you tumbled down—"

Memories of that night rushed into Jessica's mind. Mitch. She had accused him of having an affair with Amanda. And she had known, by the contempt in his voice, that he would never forgive her. She would never, as long as she lived, forget the look in his eyes. She moaned in pain, releasing Antonia's hand, and as she did, her sister said in a gentle voice, "Darling, I'm distressing you, and I mustn't." Jessica felt warm lips brush her brow. "Now lie still, try not to think, and the doctor will be right with you. I'll come in when he leaves."

With an anguished sigh, Jessica sank back on her pillows as Antonia slipped from the room. Just that one tiny exertion, grasping Antonia's hand, had exhausted her. She closed her eyes, but although she knew she oughtn't to worry, her thoughts whirled about in her head, giving her no peace.

Antonia had said Jason was fine. Her sister had never lied to her in the past, and she wouldn't lie to her now. But still... that slight change in her expression when she had asked her about Jason... what could it mean?

Try as she might, she could come up with no answer. All she could come up with were more questions. Who had found her in the pit? How long had she lain there?

Did Mitch know she was here, in hospital? It seemed
logical that he would, since her accident had happened
on his property. Was he the one who had sent for
Antonia? At least there was one thing of which she could
be absolutely sure: Antonia would not have told Mitch
about Jason. Would never have told Mitch about Jason.
Her secret would still be safe—

"Ah, young lady, so you've finally decided to rejoin
the land of the living!"

Dr. Gough was middle-aged, hearty, and blunt. He
examined Jessica thoroughly, and then sat down by the
bed and told her exactly what had happened to her.

"Three days?" Jessica ran her tongue over her parched
lips. "I've been here for three days?"

"A little over that." His eyes twinkled. "Three days
and several hours. It's almost eleven in the morning now,
and you were brought in on Monday, shortly after day-
break, when the building crew at Markington started
their work day. Fortunately the accident didn't happen
on the Friday night or the Saturday, for then there would,
in all probability, have been no one around to spot you."

So Mitch hadn't looked for her. Well, why should he
have, Jessica wondered dully, after the things she had
said to him?

She listened to Dr. Gough as he discussed her condition, explained things, but it was hard to concentrate.
She did hear him say something about her being very
lucky she hadn't caught pneumonia...temperature
almost normal again...serious bruising...no broken
bones...on the mend now—

A voice over the intercom interrupted him.

"Dr. Gough. Dr. Gough. Go to the front desk, please.
Dr. Gough to the front desk."

"No rest for the wicked!" The doctor got up from
the bed and looked down at Jessica. "I'll come back

tomorrow morning," he said. "In the meantime, take it easy."

And then he was off, stepping away briskly, leaving the door to swing shut behind him.

Jessica lay with her gaze fixed in that direction, expecting that Antonia would come in again, but when the door did open, it was to admit an attractive, brown-haired nurse with a pleasant smile.

"Well, it's good to see you awake," she greeted Jessica, adding, "I'm Nurse Edmond." As she came forward she whisked a thermometer from her pocket. "Dr. Gough tells me you can get up for a while today. How would you like to have a shower and wash your hair? I don't know about you, but after a few days in bed, that's my first priority!"

Jessica grimaced and touched a hand to her hair; it felt as lank and stringy as Antonia's had looked. "Yes, I'd like that," she said. "But my sister's waiting to see me—"

"Mrs. Redpath's gone," the nurse said. "When the doctor told her you could get up and wash your hair, she said that sounded like a good idea—she'd go back to her hotel and do the very same thing! She said to tell you she'll come back in the afternoon."

Jessica felt a dull, sinking disappointment...along with a surge of frustration. There were so many questions she wanted to ask, and only Antonia would have the answers. But she obediently opened her mouth so the nurse could pop in the thermometer, and listened as she went on chattily. "What a lovely lady she is, your sister, and so worried about you. She's hardly left your bedside since she arrived."

But even as Jessica felt her heart warm at this evidence of Antonia's love and concern, she was aware of a strange sense of unease. It didn't make sense that, after staying by her bedside so constantly, Antonia would take off as soon as she came to.

She listened to the chatting nurse with only part of her mind, the other part darting around distractedly. Something was going on. She had no proof, of course, that this was so, yet Antonia, in the first place by the giveaway expression on her face and now by her unexpected absence, had planted a seed of suspicion. Did Antonia know something she didn't want to tell her younger sister? That would certainly explain her desertion at this point. Was it possible that Antonia had left because she had known that if she stayed Jessica would be asking questions she, Antonia, didn't want to answer...and that Jessica would know by her expression that she was covering something up?

Half an hour later, back in bed with dry, shining hair and a fresh nightie, Jessica was still no closer to having an answer to the questions nagging at her. She had asked Nurse Edmond if she knew who had brought her in to the hospital, but she had said, "I'm sorry, dear, I wasn't on duty that night. Perhaps if you ask Dr. Gough tomorrow, he'll be able to tell you. Now," she went on, "let's make you comfortable—I hear the lunch trays rattling out in the corridor, you'll be getting something to eat in a minute. And afterward, why don't you have a nap, so you'll be rested up for your sister?"

There was something nice, Jessica reflected rather wearily as the nurse wheeled the narrow table up from the foot of her bed, about having your life organized by someone else. She had been in charge for the past many years...in charge of her own life and bringing up Jason...and it was a relief to give in and let someone else tell her what to do.

But just thinking of Jason set her to worrying again. When Antonia came back, in the afternoon, she would

ask her if he had settled all right at Fennie's. She had
never left him there on his own before, and she hadn't
expected to be away for more than one night. Yes, she
decided firmly as an orderly came in and placed a lunch
tray on the narrow table, she would ask Antonia about
everything in the afternoon.

And she wouldn't allow her sister to sidestep her questions. If there was something wrong, she wanted to know
about it.

When she woke, after her nap, the room was dim—no
light was on—and she sensed that it was late afternoon.

Turning her head on the pillow, she looked toward the
window, and saw that it was almost dark outside. She
had slept much longer than she'd expected to...and no
one had disturbed her. The chair by her bed was empty.
Where was Antonia? Why hadn't she come back?

Sniffing back threatening tears, Jessica brushed her
eyes abruptly with her fingertips. Feeling sorry for herself
was going to get her nowhere. But somehow, now that
the tears had started, she couldn't stop them.

She heard a sound from a dark corner of the room,
the corner by the door. Oh, Lord, a nurse was there,
had been there all the time, and had been witness to her
weakness. Throat painfully tight, Jessica turned on her
side, curling up and pulling the bed covers over her
shoulders. If she pretended she'd gone back to sleep
again, the nurse would surely leave, and would never see
the tears on her cheeks—

"Jessica..."

She froze, her breath caught in her throat as the sound
of the man's voice echoed in her head. A familiar voice.
A beloved voice. She swallowed, the burning in her eyes
becoming more intense as emotion welled up inside her.
It had sounded like Mitch, but not the angry Mitch she'd

known recently—there had been no hostility in his tone, only unhappiness and concern. She was going mad, she decided despairingly, quite mad. She was hearing things, imagining things...just because she so badly wanted Mitch, she had actually conjured up his voice.

"Jess..."

She felt a hand lightly touch her shoulder. But though the touch was light, there was a demand in it, too. And it was real. The voice she might have imagined...but not the touch on her shoulder.

In a jerky movement, she turned so she was once more lying on her back. Looking up. Looking up at the tall figure standing by the bed, only faintly discernible in the dim light. But though it was only faintly discernible, that outline could belong to only one man, and that man was Mitch. Even as her pulses began to pound out of control, she saw him reach toward the light switch—

"Don't!" Her voice was panicky, pleading. "Don't put it on."

"I want to see you, Jess."

He sounded utterly miserable. But why would he be feeling that way? He had done nothing to cause him to feel any remorse...yet it was remorse that she could hear in his voice. So...she inhaled deeply...she really was dreaming. She had not only conjured up his voice, she had also somehow managed to conjure up an image of his physical self.

"Go away," she whispered through tears. "Go away, and leave me alone."

She heard a harshly inhaled breath. "Jess, don't close me out. I need to talk with you. I need you to know how sorry I am...about everything. Especially for letting you leave, the night of the storm. God, Jess, please...give me a chance."

And it was then, as she saw him sink down on the bedside chair, his head bent over, his knuckles digging his eyes, that she knew this was no dream.

"Mitch . . . ?" She raised an arm weakly toward him. "Why are you here?"

Slowly, he lifted his head, and she saw that his eyes were dark hollows in a gaunt face. "I came because I thought . . . I hoped . . . that if we could talk, somehow we could make things come right again. If it wasn't too late." His expression was anguished.

"Oh, Mitch . . ." She couldn't bear to see him so unhappy. Couldn't bear to see his face so pale, his eyes so stark and filled with utter despair. "You've done nothing wrong," she whispered chokingly. "I'm the one who's been at fault, the one who has made all the mistakes." She reached out a shaking hand and touched his cheek, feeling as if her heart was breaking. "I believed the worst of you, without even—"

"But I did the same with you." He grasped her hand, and held it tightly as if he never wanted to let it go. "When you told me you were only out for a good time, I believed you, I didn't bother following my instincts, that warned me I was wrong. And when I saw you with Trenton, I believed what I saw, without question. Jess—" Even in the dim light she saw a glitter of desperation in his eyes. "Can we start over?"

Oh, yes, she wanted to cry. Yes, that's all I've ever wanted . . .

But he didn't know about Jason. What was he going to say when he found out she'd deprived him of the right to love his child, and have that child love him? Agony gripped her heart. She had to tell him. Tell him now. And when she did, would she see that gleam of hope in his eyes change, change to a glitter of anger . . . even rage?

She desperately fought back a sudden resurgence of her tears. "Mitch." She looked at him, her gaze beseeching. "I have something to tell you—"

Somebody clicked on the overhead light from the switch at the door. Jessica broke off abruptly, blinking in the sudden brightness. Whoever it was, she thought dully, could hardly have chosen a worse moment.

She closed her eyes, and threw her arm over her face to shut out the light...and to hide her tears. She heard the click of footsteps, and also a softer, lighter little step.

"Mummy?" A small hand touched her arm. "Mummy? Are you all right?"

Jessica felt her give a great lurch and for a moment she couldn't move. *Jason?* He was here, in this room...in the same room as...his father? Head reeling as the ramifications of the situation spun around crazily in her brain, she heard a strange, strangled sound come from her throat as she dragged her forearm from over her eyes.

Someone—Antonia—was lifting Jason up onto the bed. He clambered to lie beside her and put his arms around her neck. She felt his little body tremble, and knew that the intensity of the moment was more than he could handle.

"Shh," she whispered, drawing him to her, and holding her cheek to his, feeling their tears intermingle. "Shh, baby, it's all right now." He smelled of the outdoors, crisp, and clean, and fresh. Oh, God, how she loved him. Would always love him...just as she loved his father. "Everything's all right, darling, I won't go away again. I promise."

Her heart seemed to be swelling in her chest, as if it would burst. If only she could have spared him this trauma...

Mitch! He would see Jason, might put two and two together before she had time to explain everything. A jerk of panic shuddered through her. Wildly, she looked up, and felt stunned when she saw Fenella standing there in a cherry red coat, her eyes bright with unshed tears... tears of happiness... yet, strangely, there was also a hint of uncertainty in her expression.

"Jessie, darling." She came over and kissed her younger sister. "It's so good to see you feeling better. We've all been so worried. Jess—" she bit her lip and her eyes were pleading "—I-I'm afraid I...told Mitch...about Jason. Please try to understand. I only did what I thought best...for all of you."

At this, Jason raised his head, and said through little hiccupy sobs, "Me and Fennie came on a plane—"

"Oh, Fenella, so expensive..." The vexed words came automatically from Jessica. Part of her brain seemed to have stopped functioning; the part that had anything to do with Mitch. Oh, she could see him standing there, just to the right of Antonia, but only in her peripheral vision. She didn't want to look at him, couldn't look at him. Too much was happening, and all too fast.

"Mitch brought us down, Jess." Fenella's eyes were fixed on Jessica, anxiously. "He came up to Glengower for us. When he called to tell me about your accident, I told him I'd drive down...but he wouldn't hear of it. He insisted on coming for us. He flew up in his own plane—"

"It's spiffy, Mummy!" All of a sudden, Jason seemed to have recovered his normal bounce. "Just spiffy. And my daddy says that one day he's going to teach me to fly."

His daddy. Yes, Jessica thought dully, I'm dreaming. After all, I *am* dreaming. Any moment now I'm going to waken and find myself at home, in my flat, with the rest of my life stretching out drearily in front of me.

"Jason." It was Antonia speaking. "How would it be if you and Aunt Fennie and I go along to that nice playroom at the end of the corridor...the one we saw on the way here...with all the toys?"

Jason slid from the bed, his voice eager as he said, "Yes, let's. And then can I have some chocolate ice cream in the cafeteria?"

Fenella took his little hand, and waited a moment as he looked up at his father.

Jessica felt as if her throat was closing up. No dream, she knew at last, but wonderful, achingly wonderful reality. Her son...and his father...together. They looked like each other, both so handsome, so very dear to her...and so very much a part of herself. But why did happiness have to hurt so much?

"Are you coming with us, Daddy?" Jason asked.

Mitch crouched down to the little boy's level, and curled his hands lightly, tenderly, around his son's small shoulders. There was so much love in his eyes, love mixed with tears and an expression of awe and wonder, that Jessica thought she couldn't bear it. "Not this time, son." His voice was thick with emotion, his fingers shaking just a little as he brushed back a lock of hair that had tumbled over Jason's forehead. "I want to talk with your mother."

"OK." Jason smiled happily, all evidence of his own tears gone save for one dirty smear on his left cheek.

The three went out together, Jason chatting sixteen to the dozen, leaving Jessica alone again...with Mitch.

He watched them go, his gaze following Jason as if he could hardly bring himself to let his son leave. But when the door swung shut behind the trio, he turned, and sitting down on the chair by the bed, he leaned toward Jessica and took her hands again.

"He's everything a man could wish for in a son, and more," he said softly. "You've done a wonderful job, Jess."

"Oh, Mitch..." Jessica felt her lips tremble, and couldn't go on.

"Don't cry, Jessie," Mitch said, his mouth twisting in a kind of pain. "I never want to be the cause of your crying again."

Jessica drew one of his hands to her cheek and pressed it there, uncaring that he would feel the wet of her tears on his skin. "I'm only crying," she whispered huskily, "because I'm so happy."

"Then I withdraw what I just said." He leaned over and kissed her brow. "Because if happiness makes you cry, you've got a whole lot of crying ahead of you."

Jessica's laugh had more than a hint of tears in it. "Oh, Mitch, what a mess we've made of things, between us."

"We can thank our lucky stars that everything has turned out the way it has," he said softly.

"Still," Jessica said, shaking her head, "I didn't think Fenella would ever tell you about Jason."

"She didn't actually tell me, Jess—I guessed he was mine."

"But how—?"

"I phoned to tell Fenella about your accident, and I offered to fly up to Scotland and take her to the hospital. I couldn't understand why she seemed so panicky at the idea, and I sensed she was hiding something. For some reason, I was driven to follow up on that, and when I got there—"

"You saw Jason."

"She had never planned for me to see him. She was going to drive to Davington, and then she and Antonia were going to keep him at the hotel, take turns looking

after him while each visited you . . . and they were going
to bring him in only when they were sure I wouldn't be
here." He brushed a gentle hand over her hair, his eyes
dark with love. "But when I turned up at her flat, she
and Jason were just leaving. The moment I saw him, I
knew. He looks exactly as I did at that age, Jess, darling.
It's uncanny. And I made Fenella tell me why you had
kept it from me, that I had a son. I made her tell me
everything." His eyes darkened. "She told me how
Trenton blackmailed you. God, I wanted to kill—"

"No." Jessica stopped his angry words. "He's not
worth bothering about. We must forget all about him,
Mitch. Revenge is not sweet—"

"I guess I should feel sorry for him." A reluctant smile
curved Mitch's mouth. "One can only pity anyone who
is married to Nerine Gilbert. Now there, my darling, is
a woman who really *is* a first-class bitch!"

"Trenton told me the gist of what happened between
the two of you in the past," Jessica said quietly, "and
about how she aborted his baby . . ."

"When I found out what she had done, when I realized
how she had managed to fool me, I must admit it shook
my confidence in my own judgment." Mitch's laugh was
grim. "I decided I'd never again get seriously involved
with a woman, and marriage was definitely not going to
be an option. Which was why, when Garth and Amanda
approached me to help them out with their problem, I
didn't have to think too hard before coming to a decision. Of course, when I met you not too long after, I
fell like a ton of bricks, and despite my attempts to
remain uninvolved emotionally, all the promises I'd made
myself flew out the window—"

"Till I walked out on you." Jessica's voice was rueful.
"Oh, Mitch, what a tangled story."

"And a tangled truth that started the misunderstanding. But we'll never have any more misunderstandings. My sweet, you will marry me, won't you, and put me out of my misery?"

Jessica exhaled a contented sigh. Lying back on the soft pillows, she looked at Mitch adoringly, loving his golden eyes, loving the way they were caressing her, just as his fingers were caressing her hair, gently, reverently. "Yes, my darling...just set the date and I'll be there."

"How does three weeks Saturday sound?"

"Sounds absolutely wonderful." Jessica's voice was dreamy, soft with contentment.

"And then, my darling, we'll have our honeymoon, and since I've fixed the wedding date, I think it only fair that you should choose where we spend our honeymoon."

Jessica felt as if a faint shadow had fallen over her heart. Jason. She had only minutes ago promised she'd never leave him again, but Mitch...Mitch would want to take her on a beautiful and very special honeymoon. After all, hadn't he waited more than four years to have her all to himself...and didn't he deserve to have her all to himself, after what she had put him through?

"I think..." She hoped Mitch hadn't noticed her brief hesitation, hoped he hadn't seen, in her eyes, anything that betrayed her feelings of reluctance. "That I'd like to go back to Starlight."

"Starlight in March—that's one of the best times on the island, weatherwise. And we'll have one enormous built-in advantage." He grinned, his eyes twinkling.

What could he possibly be thinking? Jessica wondered.

He laughed, and, putting his arms around her, pulled her up against his chest. She could feel his heart thudding steadily, strongly, could feel his warmth, like a protective blanket, reach to her own heart. "Ben and Alison will, of course, come to our wedding, and we'll have them come to Markington early, so we can all spend time together, and they'll get to know Jason then, so...on our honeymoon, we'll have two built-in baby-sitters at the inn.''

"Jason...?" Jessica's voice was weak. "He can come with us? You won't mind?"

"Mind?" Mitch's eyes had become serious, more serious than she had ever seen them before. "Jessica, we—you, Jason and I—have already spent far too much time apart. We have so much to catch up on. We're a family now, and families do things together.''

"Even...honeymoon?"

"It'll be a honeymoon for three. But perhaps we will sneak away—just once—and spend a night in the log cabin. And this time, I promise you I won't leave you alone.''

"Ah, I think I still have to punish you for that," Jessica said huskily. "And the punishment will take the form of one long, lingering kiss...one for the scrapbook," she teased.

But as Mitch laughingly lowered his head, intent on succumbing to this delightfully sweet punishment, she stopped him, putting a fingertip to his lips. "There's just one thing that still intrigues me. Why was it so important that you get the Markington Estate? Surely there were others that would have served your purpose just as well?''

His arms tightened around her. "Markington Manor was Alison's home," he murmured. "It had been in her family for generations. It should have been hers, in the end, and would have been, had her father not cut her out of his will. When he died, the place fell into the hands of an American, Lester Forgan, whose Seattle-based company has branches in the U.K. He planned to settle at Markington, but for several years there have been rumors that his wife was homesick and wanted him to sell...as he did. And so the estate is back in the family now, where it should have been all along.''

''And the reason you kept it quiet that Alison was your mother was you were hoping that at some time you'd be able to buy the Markington Estate, and you didn't want would-be competitors to know of your special interest in it?''

''Mmm. Even Alison didn't know why I asked her and Ben to keep our relationship a secret. I told them that one day they'd understand. By the way—'' he grinned ''—Ben confessed to me that he'd slipped up on that score—''

''I can tell you I was stunned. I had no idea...''

''At any rate, I was able to reassure him that it was by then no longer important to keep it a secret.''

''No,'' Jessica murmured ruefully, ''you'd made sure, by taking me to the island for the day, that I would be unable to communicate with Trenton while he could still thwart you. But why did you have to leave me there overnight? Didn't the bids have to be in by midnight, on the Sunday? Midnight U.K. time?''

''Midnight in the U.S., Jess, not the U.K. All the bids were to be sent to Forgan's London lawyer and then faxed on to Forgan's head office in Seattle. So had you suspected I was on to you and you'd alerted Trenton, with the eight-hour time difference he could still have put in a second bid.''

''But why didn't you stay with me?''

''Because I knew that if I did, I'd find myself making love with you again...and I'd realized I was still *in love* with you, despite everything, and I despised myself.''

''So that's why you seemed so angry when I...seduced you...on the beach.''

"That's why, but I was determined I wouldn't let it happen again. I can tell you it was sheer torture, that night, knowing you were so close. But I was obsessed with getting Markington...for Alison's sake...and I knew I had to go through with it, keep you there, and cover all bases."

"Mitch...doesn't Alison want to live at Markington? Surely..."

"I thought at one time that she might, but she and Ben tell me that Starlight will always be their home. She's very happy with my plans for the hotel...and very happy to know that I've decided to make Markington my base. She's always felt guilty that by her actions in the past she deprived me of what she considered my rightful heritage."

"I remember your saying that Ben was Alison's second husband." Jessica frowned. "Her first...was he...?"

"He was my father. Jack McNair. He and Alison fell in love when they were just seventeen, and her parents forbade them to see each other because his father was just a gamekeeper on the estate...so Alison saw Jack in secret. She became pregnant, on purpose, hoping to put pressure on her parents to let them marry. Instead, they sent her away to a private nursing home, a place like a prison, where she was kept under lock and key. Her father's plan was that once she had the baby, it would be put up for adoption, and then Alison would be brought back home. But shortly before her due date, Alison bribed her way out of the nursing home, Jack picked her up in a borrowed car, and they got married. By that time, she was eighteen. Just days later, she went into labor, and on the way to the hospital, she and Jack were involved in a car accident—hit by a drunk driver— and Jack was killed. I was born shortly after the ambulance took Alison to Emergency. She had very serious head injuries, and when she regained consciousness after hours of intensive surgery, she discovered she was blind.''

''And there was nothing the doctors could do?''

Mitch shook his head. ''Nothing. And when they told her Jack had died, she went to pieces. She had no one to turn to, you see. Her parents had disowned her. Jack's father—a widower—would have nothing to do with her or the baby. And with the added handicap of her blindness, she realized—ironically, since this was what her father had demanded from the beginning that she do—she realized she had no choice but to put me up for adoption. She's known all along where I was, because she insisted on having a say in who the adoptive parents would be—''

''And she got in touch with you, just a few years ago?''

''Garth was the one who brought us together. Unknown to me, he had found out who my birth mother was when he was a child. He had overheard his parents, Meg and Wills, talking about me one day, talking about my mother Alison and her husband Ben, who owned a hotel on Starlight Island—''

''And Garth kept this information to himself?''

''He was just a little boy at the time. He worshipped me and was afraid that if I found out where my real mother was, I might leave home, and he couldn't have borne that. Later, as he grew older, he felt ashamed at having kept the information from me, but was afraid that if he confessed, I'd think badly of him. So...he kept it to himself...till you walked out on me and he saw how miserable I was...and he decided it was time for him to atone for what he'd done—''

''You were miserable?'' Jessica teased.

Mitch's grip on her hands tightened. ''I was *bloody* miserable,'' he said, ''you little minx—and you'd better believe it! At any rate, when Amanda miscarried at four months, Garth took her to Starlight to recuperate, booking in at the Wildings' Inn...with the intention of checking Alison out. 'Looking her over,' as he put it, before making any move. She met his exacting standards, so he arranged a private meeting with her, and urged her to contact me. She did. It made Garth very happy, knowing he'd brought us together.''

''About the conversation I overheard at Stokely Manor,'' Jessica said after a slight hesitation. ''Garth couldn't accept Amanda's pregnancy, because he felt he wasn't part of it?''

''It did cause problems—though in actual fact, asking me to be a donor had been Garth's idea in the first place—so after Amanda lost the baby, they decided not to try that route again. Decided that for them, adoption would be the way to go. And it worked out well. I'd never seen Garth more contented than he was during the last two years of his life.''

''And Amanda...she's happier now, you said?''

''She's seeing someone, an old school friend. Nothing serious...at least, not yet. She was haunted by guilt after Garth's death, remembering how unhappy he'd been during her pregnancy and feeling—foolishly—to blame. But she's come to grips with that, and now she's more like her old self, taking each day as it comes, and enjoying it.''

''Just as we are going to do.''

''Yes, my darling, just as we are going to do. Jess...''

Jessica felt her heartbeats catching as she saw a look of agony flicker in his golden eyes. What could be wrong? Was there still something she didn't know...some secret that would stand between them? She waited, her throat tight.

''When you ran away, that night, in the storm—'' Mitch inhaled a deep breath. ''I should have gone after you right away...but I didn't. You had hurt me too much. It took me some time to realize just how I had wounded you, too. In the end, I did go after you—my love for you, and my concern for you, winning out over my hurt and anger...but I should have gone sooner, and the fact that I didn't is something I'll have to live with...and regret...till my dying day—''

''Mitch—''

''Hush, darling.'' The bones of his face suddenly seemed sharper, his jaw tighter. ''Let me finish. I'd had a bit to drink that evening, so driving wasn't an option. I set off after you on foot, assuming you were making for Davington, but by the time I got to town and still hadn't found you, I decided you must have hitched a lift. I searched everywhere, went to every hotel—I was out of my mind with worry. I contacted the Davington police, but they said there was really nothing they could do.'' He raked a shaking hand through his disheveled brown hair. ''The whole thing seemed like a giant nightmare, and I hoped I'd never have to go through that kind of hell again...but then, at dawn next morning, just minutes after I got home, I saw some workmen coming up to the house, carrying your limp body.'' Mitch's voice broke, and he stopped, unable to go on.

''Oh, Mitch.'' Jessica's fingers trembled as she framed his face between her hands. ''It's all over now. You did look for me, and that's all that matters. And, darling, I've never stopped loving you, either, even in my own dark moments of despair. But now,'' she whispered huskily, ''I think we'd better have that kiss you owe me, and have it quickly, because I hear someone coming, and we wouldn't want anyone to see—''

It was quite obvious that Mitch didn't care who in the world saw. With an aching groan, he claimed her lips in a kiss that set her heart spinning crazily up to the stars, and with a feeling of unparalleled joy, Jessica slipped her arms around his neck and kissed him right back.

And when Nurse Edmonds poked her head around the door a few moments later, that efficient young woman just smiled to herself and crept quietly away.

This was *no* time, she decided sensibly, to be taking a patient's temperature.

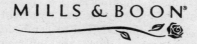

MILLS & BOON®

Next Month's Romances

Each month you can choose from a wide variety of romance with Mills & Boon. Below are the new titles to look out for next month in our two new series Presents and Enchanted.

Presents™

TOO WISE TO WED?	Penny Jordan
GOLD RING OF BETRAYAL	Michelle Reid
THE SECOND MRS ADAMS	Sandra Marton
HONEYMOON FOR THREE	Sandra Field
THE UNEXPECTED FATHER	Kathryn Ross
RYAN'S RULES	Alison Kelly
SUBSTITUTE BRIDE	Angela Devine
THE DOMINANT MALE	Sarah Holland

Enchanted™

BRINGING UP BABIES	Emma Goldrick
FALLING FOR HIM	Debbie Macomber
SECOND-BEST WIFE	Rebecca Winters
THE BABY BATTLE	Shannon Waverly
HIS CINDERELLA BRIDE	Heather Allison
MISLEADING ENGAGEMENT	Marjorie Lewty
A ROYAL ROMANCE	Valerie Parv
LIVING WITH MARC	Jane Donnelly

MILLS & BOON®

Weddings ✤ *Glamour* ✤ *Family* ✤ *Heartbreak*

Since the turn of the century, the elegant and fashionable DeWilde stores have helped brides around the world realise the fantasy of their 'special day'.

For weddings, romance and glamour, enter the world of

Weddings By DeWilde

–a fantastic line up of 12 new stories from popular Mills & Boon authors

JANUARY 1997

Bk. 7 A STRANGER'S BABY - Judith Arnold
Bk. 8 TERMS OF SURRENDER - Kate Hoffmann

Temptation ®

What better way to celebrate *the* most romantic day of the year...

My Valentine

We're delighted to celebrate this day with a wonderful collection of four short stories. Written by popular Temptation authors, these stories capture the fun, fantasy and sizzle of February 14th.

Denim and Diamonds   *by Gina Wilkins*
The Valentine Raffle   *by Kristine Rolofson*
A Very Special Delivery   *by JoAnn Ross*
Valentine Mischief   *by Vicki Lewis Thompson*

Happy Valentine's Day!

Available: January 1997   Price: £4.99

MILLS & BOON®

We are proud to announce the birth of our new
bouncing baby miniseries—

Each month we'll bring you your very own bundle of
joy—a delightful romance by one of your favourite
authors.

This exciting series is all about the true labour of
love—parenthood and how to survive it! Because, as
our heroines are about to discover, two's company
and three (or four...or five) is a family!

Look out in January 1997 for the Enchanted title:

Bringing Up Babies by Emma Goldrick

GET 4 BOOKS
AND A MYSTERY GIFT

Return this coupon and we'll send you 4 Mills & Boon Enchanted™ novels and a mystery gift absolutely FREE! We'll even pay the postage and packing for you.

We're making you this offer to introduce you to the benefits of Reader Service: FREE home delivery of brand-new Mills & Boon Enchanted novels, at least a month before they are available in the shops, FREE gifts and a monthly Newsletter packed with information.

Accepting these FREE books and gift places you under no obligation to buy, you may cancel at any time, even after receiving just your free shipment. Simply complete the coupon below and send it to:

MILLS & BOON® READER SERVICE, FREEPOST, CROYDON, SURREY, CR9 3WZ.

No stamp needed

Yes, please send me 4 free Mills & Boon Enchanted novels and a mystery gift. I understand that unless you hear from me, I will receive 6 superb new titles every month for just £2.10* each, postage and packing free. I am under no obligation to purchase any books and I may cancel or suspend my subscription at any time, but the free books and gift will be mine to keep in any case. (I am over 18 years of age)

N6LE

Ms/Mrs/Miss/Mr _____

Address _____

_____

_____

_____ Postcode _____

mps
MAILING
PREFERENCE
SERVICE

The town of Hard Luck is a town that needs women...

The 150 inhabitants are mostly male but the three O'Halloran brothers have a plan to change all that!

An exciting new mini-series in the Enchanted line, written by one of our most popular authors, **Debbie Macomber.**

"Debbie Macomber's Midnight Sons is a delightful romantic saga. Each book is a powerful, engaging story in its own. Unforgettable!"

—Linda Lael Miller

Look out for:
Because of the Baby in December 1996
Falling for Him in January 1997

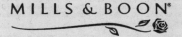

MILLS & BOON®